Oheb Shalom
Congregation

Congregation Beth Torah

Affiliated 1983

170 Scotland Road
South Orange, New Jersey

presented by

The Mills Family in
memory of
Cantor Edgar Mills

Pattern for a Heroine

Pattern for a Heroine

The Life-Story of
REBECCA GRATZ

by MIRIAM BISKIN

Union of American
Hebrew Congregations
New York

Illustrated by Bruno Frost

To

my devoted husband,

my wonderful mother,

and my patient children

Pattern
for a Heroine

CHAPTER ONE

1791

M<small>ARIA, MARIA. . . ."</small>

Rebecca stood beneath one of the casement windows of a small brick house calling up to her chum. The window was flung open, and Maria with blond curls shouted down to Rebecca with dark curls.

"I'll be right down, Rebecca. Why are you always in such a hurry?"

"Why are you always such a poke? You know we don't have all day. President Washington and the whole parade will be passing through Independence Square soon, and we won't be able to get a place to see anything."

"Oh, pooh—don't worry. Uncle Fenno's house overlooks the square, and he said we could watch from his windows. I asked him."

"Hurry, anyway. With all the people in the streets, we'll have a hard time even getting to your Uncle Fenno's. I've never seen so many people."

The upper window slammed shut, and a few moments later, a hoop-skirted young lady of twelve ran out, banging the door loudly behind her. Busily, Maria tied her blue bonnet ribbons, trying to keep up with Rebecca who was already bustling down the street.

"Rebecca, please don't rush so. I can't even catch my breath. You know how I hate being rushed—I hate it more than anything."

"Oh, Maria—I am sorry, but I just can't wait. How can you be so calm?" Rebecca's eyes shone with excitement; she turned, all smiles, waiting for Maria to catch up.

"I don't feel calm," said Maria. "I just feel rushed."

"You look just beautiful," said Rebecca. "I always love you in blue."

"You look beautiful yourself." Maria smiled in spite of herself. "Do I really look all right?" Rebecca smoothed the red velveteen of her bodice and straightened the long gleaming row of jet buttons.

"You look like a princess. I adore that dress and that color."

Rebecca dimpled with pleasure at Maria's compliments. She was a picture in her garnet velveteen frock—white lace framed the neckline and brightened the dark oval of her face. A bonnet of garnet velvet held her black curls in place, its satin streamers fastened tight under her chin. Her tiny waist was hugged tight by the velvet bodice, and small mitted hands held the billowing skirts out of the dust. Rebecca carried herself with dignity unusual for her ten years, a dignity which showed through even in her giddiest moments.

"Yes, you look like royalty—in fact a little too royal for Mister Washington, I would say. Why are you so dressed up? He won't be able to see you 'way up in the window."

"I know—but I just wanted to dress up. It isn't every day we get

4

to see the President of the United States—and he is such a great man and such a good man—my papa says he is a real friend to the Jews."

"Oh, Rebecca, must you always talk about people that way?"

"I don't mean to, Maria. It's just that Jewish people are always so happy when they find a friend. . . ." Rebecca's eyes clouded and her voice was serious.

"You not only look like royalty, you act like it. You'd think you were a Hebrew princess meant to worry about all the troubles of your people . . . like that Esther you told me about."

It was a romantic notion, but Rebecca did not argue.

"I guess that is the way we must feel," she said.

"Come on, sad eyes, enough of that! You are in Philadelphia, the city of friends. Everyone here loves the Gratzes, and everyone loves Becky Gratz as much as I do." Maria hugged Rebecca tightly.

"Oh, Maria, I love you, too, and I'm so glad you're not angry at me any more."

"Angry at you? When was I angry at you?"

"Well, this is the first time you've called me Becky this morning. I know you call me Rebecca only when you're angry at me."

"Oh, you're so smart, Becky Gratz," laughed Maria, and Rebecca laughed, too.

"Come, come, girls, you're blocking the street." Both girls turned, startled by the gruff voice behind them.

"Oh, Hyman, it's only you." Rebecca saw it was just her older brother.

"*Only* me? Is that a nice way to greet a beloved brother? Is that nice, I ask you, Miss Maria?" Hyman Gratz tipped his tall beaver and bowed low to Maria.

"Oh, Master Gratz. . . ." Maria giggled at Hyman's courtly manner, blushing a little at the flattery of his glance, very conscious now of her own new blue bengaline and lacy bonnet.

"Where are you going?" Rebecca demanded of her brother.

"Where all Philadelphia is going, little sister, to the square to see our great President Washington. But I don't think you two should go."

"Why not?" Rebecca bridled at his suggestion.

"Because, little sister, you both look so lovely that no one will even see Mister Washington. He'll be totally overshadowed, totally eclipsed. He'll have come to Philadephia for nothing."

"Oh, Master Gratz, you are a tease." Maria's face flushed a pretty pink.

"On my honor as a gentleman, I am not teasing. But if you are determined to go, let me at least escort you through the streets so that you won't be jostled or bumped."

"That would be most kind," said Maria as she gave her arm happily to this older gentleman of seventeen.

"Kind? No. You are the ones who are kind. It is my pleasure to be seen with two such charming ladies." He took each girl by the arm, and together they began to make their way to the square.

Philadelphia was an elegant city with its wide tree-shaded streets and its trim homes. Today, the city wore a shining face, scrubbed clean in honor of the great man who was to arrive shortly. The marble doorsills, the windows, even the street lamps sparkled in the sunlight; the lawns shone green and trim unmarred by any stray leaf or twig. The spring air was fragrant with the lilac and honeysuckle that grew in clumps and cascades in every garden. Shop windows were diamond-clean showcases for displays honoring the President and his gracious ladies.

Hyman and Maria and Rebecca made their way through the crowds, chattering gayly, filled with the exhilaration of the day. As they came to James Fenno's house, Hyman prepared to leave them.

"Won't you come in, Master Hyman?" said Maria. "I know Uncle Fenno won't mind."

"Nothing would please me more," said Hyman, "but I promised to meet two fellows at the inn."

"Fellows—hmph—that's a likely story," said Rebecca.

"Be nice, Becky," said Hyman. "Don't lose your sweet ways, and keep your mind on your own concerns."

"Are you sure you must go?" said Maria.

"Very sure, sweet Miss Maria, although I would like nothing more than to stay." Hyman patted Maria's mitted hand, doffed his hat, and shouldered his way back into the crowd.

"He's so nice," sighed Maria as she grasped the wrought iron leonine knocker and rapped loudly. The door opened, and an elderly gentleman with a cane beckoned them in.

"Oh, girls, I was getting worried. The streets are so crowded. I'm so glad that you are here."

"And we are so glad to be here!" Maria threw herself at her uncle, hugging him impulsively.

James Fenno was a handsome man despite his seventy years. He was stooped and had to walk with a cane, but he still looked directly at the world with keen blue eyes and still spoke in a firm, steady voice.

"La-de-da, Maria, don't knock an old man off his feet. I'm not used to such violent love-making—not that I don't enjoy it, of course. Don't you have a kiss for me, too, Miss Rebecca?"

"Of course, Master Fenno." Rebecca leaned forward so that the old man could kiss her cheek.

"Now my day is complete," said Uncle Fenno as the girls giggled. "Come, let me take you up to my parlor. Isn't that what the spider says to the fly?"

The girls giggled again. They followed Uncle Fenno up the carpeted staircase to a large room with a balcony overlooking the square. In front of the long glass doors leading on to the balcony was a low table set with a lace cloth and a tea service and a bouquet of white lilacs. There was also a silver tray of small sandwiches and cookies.

"I know young ladies like to nibble so I thought we could have a party. And, Rebecca, you don't have to worry. My kind Jewish neighbor, Mrs. Seixas, prepared everything in her own kitchen and brought it over. These are even her dishes and her silver. Wasn't she nice to help an old man? Probably thought I wouldn't be too good at entertaining young ladies." His blue eyes twinkled as he sat down in his own chair and his two young guests seated themselves primly at either side of the table.

"Oh, Master Fenno, you are good at everything," Rebecca smiled happily, her face lighted by her own sweet nature.

Master Fenno nodded. "No one would contradict such a wise woman in her wisdom, would they, Maria?"

Maria smiled, too. "But you are good, Uncle Fenno, and very kind."

"And a lot sweeter in such good company, I must say."

Rebecca found this all very pleasant; Uncle Fenno treated them both as though they were real adults. What was he saying?

"I can't tell you how thoughtful it was of you to come to spend time with an old gentleman."

"You were the thoughtful one, Uncle Fenno, for having us."

"Yes, Master Fenno, you were the thoughtful one, a very good friend." Rebecca loved Maria's gentle uncle.

"You know, Rebecca, being friends with the Gratzes is a custom in our family. Why, I knew your father when he first came to America. He and my son, James, have always done business together and now you and Maria are friends. It seems to be a long-standing habit."

"See, Rebecca," said Maria, "I told you that the Gratzes had friends, and you and I will be friends always, just as your daddy and my daddy and uncle have always been."

Rebecca listened with a smile. What a day to remember this would always be!

★　★　★　★

The girls could never have dreamed, never have anticipated the color and pomp of the President's parade, and they watched wide-eyed as the flower floats passed in review. First came a floral platform festooned with bunting and blue ribbon and dedicated to Betsy Ross. Seated in the center of the platform was a dark-haired girl stitching on an American flag. Then came a replica of the liberty bell constructed of papier-mâché and painted a bronze color. The bell's stand and the entire platform were covered with yellow and white chrysanthemums, and standing on this carpet of blossoms was the bell-ringer, a small and handsome little boy attired in white satin breeches and a royal blue satin waistcoat. Then came a white daisy replica of Mount Vernon, the President's home in Virginia, and then floats showing the founding of Pennsylvania by William Penn, floats in tribute to Ben Franklin, Philadelphia's aged patriarch, and to John Adams, the new vice-president.

Rebecca and Maria "oohed" and "aahed" at Philadelphia's fire guard marching along smartly with the sun glinting on their brass helmets and brass-buttoned red uniforms. The girls applauded the first horse-drawn fire wagon in the new colonial states and cheered at the remarkable prowess of the Pennsylvania state horse militia.

But then came the great moment of the day. Jubilant cheers of welcome rose from the crowd. Rebecca and Maria leaned far over the railing to catch that first glimpse, and suddenly there he was, President Washington riding into view, sitting proudly erect astride his great white charger, waving his tricorne gayly at the citizenry. Martha Washington followed in her carriage, nodding and smiling, and lifting her mitted hand in a gentle gesture of friendship. The rays of the sun seeping through her blue lace parasol made a shining pattern on her heavy white hair and glinted on the heavy gold brooch that held a blue lace shawl on her shoulders. The blue skirts of her crinoline billowed off in soft folds all around her.

"Oh, Maria, isn't she beautiful?"

"Yes, and isn't he handsome?"

9

"Oh yes, yes."

"Maria, he's looking up! He sees us!" Rebecca was squealing.

"Silly, he's not looking at anyone special."

"He is! He is! Look! He's waving again."

"Wave back, wave back!"

Rebecca raised her hand, and for a moment, it did seem as though the great man was smiling right at them.

The girls waited with Uncle Fenno for the crowds to thin out. The spring dusk fell quickly, and the lamplighters were making their rounds as the two friends hurried home.

CHAPTER TWO

A Higher Price

THE WALK HOME WAS FILLED WITH EXCITED CHATTER AND GAY reminiscenses of the wonderful day.

"I didn't think he was such a tall man," mused Rebecca.

"Or so handsome. If I were Mrs. Washington, I'd be so proud. . . ."

"So should I, but who wouldn't be proud of such a husband, a man who's done so much for his country. . . ."

And so they talked as they walked, arms interlocked, until they came to Maria's door.

"Hurry, Becky," said Maria, "I want you to get home before dark."

"Don't worry, Maria."

"I do worry. After all, I'm older than you."

"A whole two years—that's not even enough to count."

"Well, it does count, and you do as I say. Hurry now."

11

"I will and don't worry. I have only a little way to go."

Rebecca turned and ran, her red skirts flying up over her lacy pantaloons. In a few moments she was at her own familiar door.

Something was strange. There were no lights in the front of the house.

"Mother," she called as she entered the foyer.

"In here, dear." It was Papa's voice.

Rebecca hurried to the large dining room at the rear of the house and found everyone seated at the large round mahogany table. For a moment, Rebecca thought she was late for dinner, but then she saw that the table was not even set. She looked from one face to another—Hyman, Jac, Jo, Simon, Frances, Richea, Rachel, even little Ben—all so serious, and Mother, her eyes red and puffed and her cheeks streaked with tears. Grandpa Simon sat in a chair in the corner, rocking back and forth, praying to himself. Tears had wet his bearded and wrinkled cheeks, too, but he made no move to wipe them away.

"Mama, Grandpa, what's wrong? Tell me what's wrong." Rebecca looked from one to the other, her heart beating fast with fright.

"My sister Shinah is dead." Mama Gratz dropped her face into her hands.

"Aunt Shinah? No, she can't be." Rebecca was caught by the sudden hollow shock. How could Aunt Shinah be dead? She was so gay and so full of smiles, so alive! She couldn't be dead.

"To me she is. And she's killed your Grandpa, too."

"Ssh, Miriam, you are upset. You should not say such things to a child. You do not mean it." Michael Gratz took his wife into his arms, holding her close, murmuring comfort into her ear as though she were a hurt child.

"My sister. How could she do such a thing to us? And to Grandpa Simon? It is breaking his heart. It will kill him."

"Daughter, I will live. This is God's will, and we must accept it." The old man's voice was thin and cracked, but it did not waver.

12

"Will someone please tell me what has happened." Rebecca turned to Simon, her fright giving way to puzzlement.

Simon bit his lip; he did not look up or answer.

"Aunt Shinah is married to Dr. Nicolas Schuyler," Hyman whispered softly.

"But she couldn't be. He is not Jewish."

"No, he is a Gentile," said Papa.

"But why should she marry him?" Rebecca thought of all the handsome young Jewish gentlemen who had sought Aunt Shinah's hand.

Hyman shrugged.

"Who knows?" said Jac. "At any rate, she is now Mistress Nicolas Schuyler."

"May she never have a moment's happiness!" Miriam Gratz sobbed.

"Mother, you don't mean that." Rebecca knew how her mother felt, but such words shocked her. Aunt Shinah had gone down a path from which there was no turning back, a path which would take her from her family forever. It was as if she was lost to them all, for she had forsaken her responsibilities and deserted her heritage.

But Rebecca hated to see her mother so distraught; she knew Mother would never forgive Aunt Shinah as long as there was breath in her body. Rebecca wanted to cry, too.

"What difference does it make?" Hyman spoke in a whisper to Jo.

Joseph shrugged.

"A lot of difference," snapped Richea, her dark eyes flashing. "What would become of us if all Jews married Gentiles?"

"Yes," added Rachel, "and what of their children? They won't be Jews, either."

"Poor Aunt Shinah," sighed Rebecca, "poor Mother!"

"She was bad to hurt our mommy," little Ben chimed in.

"Ssh," said Rebecca. "No one was bad. No one meant to hurt anyone."

"She hurt Grandpa, too," Ben insisted.

"Ssh, little one. You talk too much," admonished Simon.

"Stop it, all of you," ordered Papa Gratz. "And Mama, listen to me. You must remember your sister is not a child; she knew what she was doing. Perhaps you should pray that she will have the courage and forbearance to live up to all the promises she has made."

"Pray for her? There are no prayers in my heart for her. She is no longer my sister. She never was my sister." And Mama's sobs broke out anew.

★   ★   ★   ★

Late that night, after everyone had gone to bed, Rebecca lay awake in the dark. She heard the clock strike eleven, then twelve; she heard a board creak, someone was on the stairs. Perhaps it was someone she could talk with, someone with whom she could share her troubled thoughts. She slipped into her white challis wrapper, lighted a taper, and crept softly down the stairs. There was a light in the library, and through the half-open doorway, she could see her father seated before the hearth. He was deeply absorbed in thought, staring at the red dying embers but seeming not to see them at all.

"Papa," Rebecca said softly.

"Yes, child."

"Please don't worry. . . ."

"At this moment, I think being a father means being worried."

"Why is Mother so upset?"

"Her sister married a Gentile."

"But we have many Gentile friends. Doesn't Mama like them?"

"Of course, she does, my child. We have many Gentile friends whom we like and love, but your mother feels that a Jew should remain a Jew, and a Christian a Christian."

"Do you feel that way, too, Papa?"

"Very much so, my dear. A Jew can only carry out his covenant

14

to God through his children, through his own religious faith. There is no other way."

There was a long silence, and Rebecca snuggled closer to her father's knee.

"And your mother knows, too, that such marriages demand a price more than most people can pay."

"Pay?"

"Yes. In a good marriage you give your whole self. If you marry someone who believes as you do, this giving unites you both into a stronger force. But if you marry someone who does not believe as you do, you face a lifetime of concession—of explaining what you believe only to have it dismissed or forgotten or tolerated. That is a high price to pay for love."

"Doesn't Aunt Shinah know this?"

Michael Gratz patted Rebecca's head and sighed. "She knows it, but for the moment, she does not think it is important. People in love are blinded to everything but what they choose to see. She isn't thinking about much now except her own emotions, and I doubt that she has even considered that there may be a yet higher price to pay."

"A higher price?"

"Yes. The love for which she has paid so much may fade or, even worse, turn to hate. Then she will have purchased nothing; nothing but pain and suffering. That is what your mother fears, and what I fear for my children." Papa Gratz suddenly looked old and tired.

"You know," he continued, "all I want for any of you is that you be as happy as Mama and I. We have had ten children, and we have had many problems and many quarrels, but on the Sabbath, as we look across the table at each other, we know we are united by an even stronger force than our love for each other."

"More than love, Papa?"

Papa stroked Rebecca's silky hair with gentle hands. "Yes, my child, more than love for each other, and more than the love we

15

have for our family, we are joined together by our love for God."

Rebecca looked up at Papa's tired face, tears spilling from her dark eyes. "Papa, that is what I want, too."

And in her ten-year-old heart, that is the kind of life she prayed she would have.

CHAPTER THREE

A Yellow Bonnet

THINGS WERE MUCH THE SAME THE NEXT MORNING. MAMA AND the girls were crying; Papa and the boys were eager to be out of the house even earlier than usual. Grandpa Simon sat on a small bench, praying silently; he had neither eaten nor slept nor washed nor combed himself.

"Oh, Grandpa," cried Rebecca. "Things aren't so bad, really they aren't."

"Rebecca!" Her mother's voice was soft yet warning. "Do not try to console him foolishly. Such a man can accept the will of God."

"But Aunt Shinah is not dead. Why should he mourn her so?"

"She is dead to him and to me." Mama turned her back, and Rebecca knew the matter was to be discussed no further.

17

"Miss Becky," called a voice from the kitchen, "is that you? I want you right in here to eat your breakfast."

"Yes, Sally," said Rebecca. Even Sally, the cook, didn't sound very genial this morning.

"I do declare," she was muttering as Rebecca pushed the door open. "You young 'uns are just ungrateful. Here old Sally made you all a nice breakfast and all you do is let it get cold."

Little Ben was already at the table listening to her recital, but evidently it had little effect for he was spooning through his porridge idly and without enthusiasm.

"Master Ben, I told you to eat, and I mean eat. You're a'playin'."

"I'm just not hungry, Sally," he said, bowing his head further over the bowl, hiding his tears.

"Neither am I, Sally," said Rebecca.

"Well, if that don't beat all. Ben, quit salting your oatmeal. If you don't want to eat, don't. But don't cry over it, neither. Miss Rebecca, how would you like to take Master Ben for a walk in the park? Maybe he'll feel better."

"I'd love to. Want to go with me, Ben?"

"Yes, oh, yes. I'd like that."

"Good. Get your cap and I'll tell Mama."

"I'll tell your maw, Miss Becky. You go get your things and I'll fix you and Master Ben some jelly sandwiches to eat in the park."

"Wonderful!" Rebecca flew up the stairs for her bonnet and shawl.

She could see her mother ushering some elderly gentlemen into the living room to see Grandpa Simon. Their faces were somber and their demeanor solemn. Rebecca knew that they had come to be with Grandpa in his time of sorrow. Mama nodded sadly to whatever they were saying, and Rebecca was glad that she and Ben were on their way out of the house.

Ben half-pulled, half-dragged Rebecca along the cobbled walks

18

of Chestnut Street. "Come, simmer down," said Rebecca, "walk a little slower so I can see things."

"All right," said Ben slowing down to what seemed to him a snail's pace. There were few people out so early, but Rebecca did not mind; she rather enjoyed the quiet of early morning. The bell on Independence Hall chimed the hour, and she saw here and there a merchant beginning to do his shop-opening chores for the day.

She paused before the milliner's window. Nestling on a green velvet drape was the most beautiful bonnet she had ever seen—a floral confection made completely of straw lace and yellow silk poppies.

"Ben, isn't it beautiful?"

"Ummm." Seven-year-old Ben evidently wasn't impressed with bonnets.

"I wonder if a young lady I know would like that bonnet," a deep, familiar voice asked.

"Oh, Papa," said Rebecca, turning around quickly to hug her father. "Do you mean I could have it? It's so beautiful!"

"Almost beautiful enough for my daughter. Shall we go in, Benjamin, and check the price?"

"Are we buying Becky a present?"

"Maybe, would you like to do that?"

"Oh, yes, Sir." Ben grasped his father's big hand in his small one and tugged away. "Come on, let's go in."

The little shop bell tinkled, and the shop mistress with a striped apron over her black dress hurried out to serve them.

"Miss Percival, I would like you to meet my daughter and my son." Rebecca looked at her father and thought what a handsome man he was in his gray morning coat with its flaring skirt and his tight oxford trousers. No dandy wore whiter shirts or shinier boots than Papa; and when the ladies saw his black curly hair which was getting a little gray and his sharp black eyes, and heard his won-

19

derful deep voice, you could see how impressed they were—even a little old lady like Miss Percival, the shopkeeper.

"I don't think so, Mister Gratz," Miss Percival was saying, "but I am most happy to make their acquaintance. How do you do, children?"

Rebecca dropped a prim curtsy, and Ben bowed in his best company manner. Miss Percival smiled approvingly.

"Your youngsters have beautiful manners, Mister Gratz."

"Thank you, Ma'am. That is a tribute to their mother."

Mother. . . . At the sound of the word, Rebecca was struck with wonder. She had forgotten all about Mama and Aunt Shinah and everyone. . . .

"Now, Mister Gratz, how may I serve you?" Miss Percival was saying.

"Well, it seems there is a yellow bonnet in the window that has captivated a certain young lady."

"Oh, yes," said Miss Percival. "Isn't it lovely? I just finished it yesterday. It should look lovely with your daughter's dark hair."

Before she knew what was happening, Rebecca was seated before the large oval mirror with the yellow poppies perched on her black curls.

"Do you like it, Becky?" asked Papa.

"I love it," said Rebecca, "but it must cost a great deal."

"No amount of money is too much to pay for a smile like the one you're wearing now. Your face seemed pretty long when I saw you standing outside."

"It was, I guess. You know Mama and Grandpa. . . ."

"I know . . . I know . . . but how about the bonnet? Miss Percival is waiting."

"I'd love it, but is it all right? I feel odd with Mama so sad and all, for me to be so happy."

"Becky looks pretty," said Ben.

"You're right, Ben, she does, and there's nothing wrong in looking pretty and being happy. Becky, you didn't cause your mother's

20

unhappiness. You shouldn't feel guilty about it. There isn't anything you can do about it either, so don't carry the weight of the world on your shoulders."

"Yes, Papa." How wonderful could one man be!

"We'll take the bonnet, Miss Percival," said Papa, reaching into his purse for some money which he put into the woman's hand.

★　★　★　★

"Oh, Papa, it was so expensive," said Rebecca as the shop door tinkled behind them.

"Not really," said Papa. "Things you can buy are rarely expensive. It's the things you can't buy that are usually dear."

Rebecca nodded. She was not quite sure what he meant, but she knew it had something to do with Mama and Grandpa and Aunt Shinah.

"Can you come to the park with us, Papa?" asked Ben. "We have jelly sandwiches."

"I'm sorry. It would be a treat, but I have to miss it today. You know I have a business to run. I will walk part of the way with you, though."

The three walked along together, Rebecca reveling in her own reflection in every shop window, and Ben happy simply to hold his father's hand and chatter to him about all the important happenings in his young boy's world.

"How could any of us ever hurt him?" thought Rebecca. "No one ever had a father like ours . . . no one in the world."

CHAPTER FOUR

1796

MAMA GRATZ NEVER MENTIONED AUNT SHINAH'S NAME AGAIN. Day followed day, week followed week. It was Purim, then Pesach, then Yom Kippur . . . and the years went by. Shinah never forgot Mama's children; there were always birthday gifts and notes, and although Miriam did not encourage her family to answer, neither did she discourage them.

"It's worse than if she were dead," Rebecca confided to Maria. "It's as though she never existed at all. It's horrible that this could happen to two sisters."

Maria nodded, "I wonder what it's like being married to such an important man." Maria was now seventeen, and all that was important in her life was romance and love. At times, she seemed silly to Rebecca's not-yet-interested fifteen.

"You should see the letters she writes—all about the balls and receptions at the Governor's mansion at Albany. He seems to be related to everybody who is anybody and the places they go—to the opera in New York City, to the spa at Saratoga, just everywhere."

Maria had heard all this before, but she sat enthralled. It was like a fairy tale, and Shinah was the exiled princess.

"Does she ever ask for your mama in her letters?"

"Always. In every letter she asks for Mama and Grandpa Simon, and she always sends them her love."

"Do you tell your mama?"

"I don't dare. Not even Hyman and Jac say anything about seeing Shinah and I know they visit her every time they go North. Jac says you can't imagine how beautiful their home is. It's about six miles north of Albany, right on the Hudson River. They own acres and acres of land with horses and everything. I'd love to visit them, I really would."

Late one afternoon, when Rebecca arrived home, she found a small envelope on the hall table addressed to her. The penmanship was ladylike and fine. It was from Aunt Shinah.

Ripping the envelope open, she read the note with growing excitement.

Niece Rebecca,

Dr. Schuyler and I would be most honored to have you visit us the month of June.

That will be after your birthday, but we felt that the summer weather would be more enjoyable than the middle of March which marks *your* day. March here is often very dreary and snowy and no time to see the beauties of the North. You will find a coach passage enclosed which is our gift to you, one I hope you can enjoy. My very best regards to all your family, especially your mama and grandpa. I anxiously await your reply.

Your loving
Aunt Shinah

Rebecca ran to the library. Papa was seated at his desk reading.

"Papa," Rebecca cried, "look at this note. Read it. It's from Aunt Shinah. She wants me to visit her."

"That's nice," said Papa. Rebecca could not read a reaction in his voice.

"May I go, Papa, may I? Would Mama give her permission?"

"Of course you may go. Mama won't keep you away. I've told you before, she doesn't want you to shoulder her problems. She is a very fair woman, and she would not want to influence your feelings. Shinah is your aunt, and if you wish, you may visit her."

Rebecca walked slowly up the stairs to her room. Why did she feel guilty when she wanted to be gay? Why couldn't she just forget everything and be excited?

"I'll take this . . . and this . . . and . . . this," she talked to herself as she pulled frock after frock out of the closet.

"Shall we move the whole house for you, Sis?" Hyman poked his head in the doorway. "Papa tells me you're headed North for high society."

"Oh, I am, Hyman, isn't it wonderful?"

"Sure is. Aunt Shinah and Uncle Nicolas will give you a good time. When are you going? Tomorrow?"

"Not until the first of June."

"But this is only March."

"I know, but it takes time to pack for a trip like this."

"Well, I wouldn't disturb you for the world. If I go, you should be able to do all your chores in three months."

"Funny, very funny. Just go if you don't want to help."

"I'll help. What shall I do?"

Rebecca sent Hyman to the attic for a trunk. When Jo appeared, he was sent for a bandbox and Ben for a valise. Frances arrived with her ribbons and Richea with her jewelry. Soon the bedroom was a mass of strewn finery and luggage.

"You'd better sleep in my room tonight, Becky," laughed Frances, "I can't even find your bed."

24

Rebecca looked around at them all, laughing, smiling, joking, happy—and she loved them all. This was her family, her very own, her dear brothers and sisters—her everything.

The next weeks were a flurry of activity from which Mother kept aloof. At last the day came when Rebecca's bags and valises and boxes stood waiting in the hall. Jac was outside with the buggy waiting to drive her to the coach depot. Mama had to say something, or else Rebecca knew she would unpack every bit of clothing and stay home.

"Mama," she called upstairs.

"Here I am, Rebecca." Mama must have been standing in the hall all the time.

"Mama." Why couldn't Rebecca say what she wanted to say? That she loved Mama most of all; that she would stay home if Mama wished; that she wouldn't hurt Mama for the world.

"Have a good trip, my child."

Rebecca kissed Mama gently, placing her fingers on her mother's cheek. She felt tears.

"Don't cry, Mama," Rebecca whispered.

"No, my child, I won't. Journey safely and hurry back to me."

"I will, Mama, I will."

Rebecca watched Mama wave from the window, watched even after she could no longer see the house. She felt more lonely than she had ever felt in her life—leaving Mama, leaving the family. It was only for a month, but it seemed like forever.

★　★　★　★

As the coachman drove through the long rows of elms that marked the entrance to the Schuyler estate, Rebecca wondered about Aunt Shinah. Had she changed? Six years is a long time. . . . Rebecca wondered if she would know her aunt. There, on the Schuyler veranda, was a lady who had to be Shinah. She was wearing her heavy black hair coiled high in a gleaming swirled coif and a heavy rose-colored damask dressing gown covered from neck to

25

As the coachman drove. . . .

hem with a film of rosy lace. Rebecca had never seen such a gown. Shinah waved a slim hand, a jeweled accessory to this splendid picture.

The coachman helped Rebecca from the carriage as Shinah came down the veranda steps.

"Oh, Becky, I am so glad you are here." Rebecca was enveloped in a cloud of rose lace and lavender perfume. "You are beautiful . . . a real young lady."

"Have I changed, Aunt Shinah?" Rebecca asked.

"Oh yes, but I would know you anywhere . . . you look just like your mother." Shinah stood back to look at her niece.

"Have I changed, Becky?" she said.

"I think you have," Rebecca said hesitatingly. "You are even lovelier than I remembered, and so splendid."

Shinah's laugh was a tinkle of approval at her niece's compliment.

"Come, you must meet Uncle."

She chattered away as she led Rebecca through room after room carpeted in heavy Aubusson and lighted by gilt candelabra. The silken damask drapes, the ornate furniture, the array of bric-a-brac all showed Rebecca clearly that Uncle Nicolas was a most successful man.

"Nicolas is a physician, you know, my dear, and a very busy man. Besides his practice, he has great family responsibilities—the Schuyler holdings and all."

"Yes," said Rebecca, not knowing what else to say.

"And of course, we must entertain all the time. So much of what is politics has to be accomplished socially. . . ." Aunt Shinah's rings flashed with dazzling brilliance as she talked. Rebecca was fascinated by her aunt as she would be by a bright jeweled bird.

"Ah, yes, Uncle is such an important man. Here is his study. I will knock in case he is busy. You know how men are."

Rebecca stood beside Shinah as her aunt tapped lightly on the heavy door.

27

"Come in," said a man's deep voice.

"Dear," said Shinah, pushing the door ajar, "here is our niece, Rebecca."

"Ah, Niece Rebecca, it is so good to see you."

Nicolas Schuyler pushed his heavy leather chair back from his desk and rose to greet Rebecca, his hand extended in welcome. He is so tall and quite distinguished looking, thought Rebecca, noting the broad shoulders and the graying temples. His profile was finely chiseled, and his mouth full and smiling. His voice was deep and low, and Rebecca tried not to stare at his hands. They were as white and carefully manicured as Shinah's. Truly Uncle Nicolas was an aristocrat.

"How do you like our little place, Niece Rebecca?" he said, his tones carefully modulated by education and family breeding.

"It doesn't seem little, Uncle Nicolas, but it is very beautiful."

"It is, indeed, and your Aunt Shinah is responsible. I'm busy a good deal, as you know, and she runs this place like a clock. Never leaves a thing undone."

"Yes, Grandfather Simon always called her his little *balabusta*."

"His what?"

"Balabusta, dear. . . . It's a Yiddish word that means a good housewife. It's a compliment." Shinah laughed rather self-consciously as she explained Rebecca's comment.

"I'm sure it is. *Balabusta*—is that it? How quaint!"

Somehow Rebecca was annoyed with the handsome man behind the desk, and surprised at herself because she was annoyed. Why did his tone bother her? Uncle Nicolas was nice. He was kind and good. He meant nothing by his remark, and yet he annoyed her. Why? Why? It must have been his tone she found annoying, that slight note of tolerance when something Jewish was mentioned; and she found herself annoyed also with Aunt Shinah and her self-conscious subservience. Papa had said marriage could change people, and this must be part of the change.

Rebecca could not help but note the things that were missing—

no *mezuzot* hung over the doors, no Shabbat candles lighted on Friday night, no blessings at mealtimes. The closeness to God that Rebecca had always felt was not present in this house.

Rebecca's meals were prepared separately by Aunt Shinah herself. Usually, she ate fish or eggs, but she did not mind. Very little was said about her dietary preferences, until one evening when they all sat down to dinner and Uncle Nicolas began to carve a succulent roast of beef.

"This is beautiful, Becky," he said. "Won't you have just a slice?"

"I'd rather not," said Rebecca.

"I feel so guilty," said Shinah, "eating all this in front of you."

Rebecca looked at her aunt in amazement. Aunt Shinah was glittering in her green damask dress with her emerald earbobs catching the reflection of candlelight. Her hair had never been so black and shining, and Rebecca stared. Aunt Shinah was someone else. She was a stranger—a lovely woman but a stranger.

"I've had more than enough, Aunt Shinah," Rebecca replied.

"The beef is truly delicious, Niece Rebecca. Sure you won't change your mind?" The slice Nicolas extended was pink and dripping in its own juice.

"Many of my Jewish friends eat at my table. Why, I know that even your brothers would not refuse."

"Nicolas!" Shinah was annoyed.

"I'm sorry, my dear."

"Don't be sorry, Uncle Nicolas. I know that my brothers are not always as observant as we would like them to be. It distresses Papa and Mama." Rebecca bent her head over her platter.

"Well, I'm glad to see that you are better than they." Nicolas leaned across the table to pat her hand. Rebecca pulled back unconsciously from his patronizing gesture.

"No, this doesn't make me better. I follow the rules of my faith because it is my pleasure and my desire. But it would be a sin for me to judge what others do or do not do in their obligation to

29

God." Rebecca flushed. She sounded so holier-than-thou and she didn't mean to. It was just how she felt. She wouldn't want them to think that she was trying to hurt them; but she had spoken out in truth, that was all.

The rest of the meal was silent, but after dinner the usual stream of guests began to arrive—the Livingstons, the Ten Eycks, the Van Nesses, and the Van Burens—all the notables who were constant visitors to the mansion of her aunt and uncle. Rebecca was aware of their prominence and impressed by their wealth and position, but tonight she felt very much set apart.

After the company had departed, Rebecca sat before the dressing table mirror brushing her long hair. There was a soft tap at the door.

"Yes?" she said.

The door opened, and Aunt Shinah stepped in. She held a lighted taper in her hand, and, in her white robe, she looked even more lovely than she had at dinner.

"Becky, I have a surprise for you," she said.

"Oh, really, Aunt Shinah, what is it?"

"How would you like to go to Saratoga?"

"I would love it. But what about Uncle Nicolas? Can he get away?"

"Well not really, but it was your Uncle Nicolas's idea. You know he is always so good and wonderful, and he thought you should see our spa before you go home. He says there's nothing finer in all of Europe. You know the Schuylers go to Europe all the time. But he thought it would be nice for you."

"Oh, it would, it would, if only he doesn't mind your being away. I know Papa hates to have Mama go away for long."

"Well, we won't be gone long enough for him to miss me." Rebecca saw tears shining in Aunt Shinah's eyes, but why should Aunt Shinah cry? She had everything she ever wanted. Perhaps it was only the reflection of the candle or perhaps just her own imagination.

When Rebecca awoke the next morning, Aunt Shinah already had the maids pressing clothes and packing bags, and by noon the groom brought around the carriage and the horses, and they were off to Saratoga. The day was sunny and warm, and Shinah chattered almost as rapidly as the horses' hoofs. She pointed out every landmark on the way—the homes where George Washington had stayed, the landgrants of the original patroons, the route of the Continental Army during the Revolution. . . . Rebecca watched and listened, fascinated to see places she had heard of so often.

It was after dark when their carriage pulled up to a spacious hotel. The huge veranda was lighted by gas lamps, and Rebecca could see the swaying figures of dancers through the long windows.

"Look, Aunt Shinah, look at the dancers."

"Wait until you see the ballroom, child. It is magnificent, all mirrors and crystal chandeliers."

"Which hotel is this?"

"The Grand Hotel. It's supposed to be one of the most sumptuous in the world."

"Oh, it must be."

Rebecca and Shinah followed a Negro porter in uniform as a Negro groom in livery took their carriage and horses. Rebecca's feet sank into the thick red carpets.

"What luxury!" she sighed.

Aunt Shinah laughed indulgently.

"Aren't you thrilled, Aunt Shinah?"

"I guess I'm used to it. I know it's very nice, but I'm not thrilled any more."

Rebecca again thought she saw tears in her aunt's eyes, but it couldn't be.

★   ★   ★   ★

Saratoga was a spectacular place, as lovely as all the descriptions written of it, thought Rebecca, as she and Shinah strolled in Congress Park, past the crimson geranium beds and the fountains, under the archways made by the huge elms. Many a gentleman's

31

eye was caught by the two dark-haired ladies under the lacy para-sols. Sixteen and twenty-six, a belle and a matron—both so alike they might be sisters, and both striking.

"Mama would enjoy this so much," said Rebecca. "You know she loves flowers."

"She loves everything," said Shinah, "but me."

Rebecca could say nothing. She thought of her mother, and how tired she often looked.

"How is your mama?" asked Shinah.

"She works very hard."

"Yes, for Papa and the children. It must be wonderful."

"Not as wonderful as your life, Aunt Shinah."

Shinah seemed very far away for a moment. Then she replied, "Your mother knows the joy of being needed."

"But," said Rebecca, "Dr. Schuyler needs you. . . ."

"Nicolas needs no one. He has wealth, position, friends. He is a Schuyler, that is all he needs."

"He needs your love, I am sure." Rebecca put her warm hand on her aunt's.

"I wish I were as sure. A man needs a family more than a woman. Nothing seems to have worked out as we planned." This time Rebecca was sure of the tears in Aunt Shinah's eyes.

"Perhaps, someday. . . ." She hated to see Shinah cry.

"Perhaps, who knows? It may be just as well. It may be God's will that there are no children to be pulled this way and that by things they don't even understand." Shinah daubed at her eyes with a tiny bit of lace and cambric.

"But enough," she said, "I mustn't burden a young thing like you on such a day." She fixed her usual bright smile on her face. "Would you like to have dinner at the Casino? I can point out all the famous people who vacation here . . . and. . . ."

Rebecca nodded absently as Shinah prattled on. She thought back to that night so long ago in the library with Papa. This was what he had meant when he said such a marriage demanded tremendous sacrifice, the kind that can often destroy the happiness of any man or woman.

The visit to Saratoga was an experience for Rebecca as was the whole month with the Schuylers. It was not like visiting her other aunts or her sister, Richea, whose home was already filled with bouncing babies and candle-lighted holiday observances. These were familiar warm places where one did not have to be wary that some unwitting remark would be offensive. Despite the pomp and grandeur of the Schuyler home, and the never-ending flow of impressive guests, Rebecca was glad when her visit ended.

Memories of the days she had spent with the Schuylers always filled her with sadness. The life for which they surrendered so much had given them each so little. Perhaps it was because they had so little to share, not a common tradition, not a common heritage, not even a common identity. Some things were evidently beyond the strength and planning of human beings.

CHAPTER FIVE

Practical Considerations

"SHINAH HAS SO MUCH," REBECCA CONFIDED IN MARIA, "AND yet she has so little."

"Well," said Maria, "you have to remember that we all can't have everything. As marriages go, it's probably as satisfactory as most."

Rebecca was disturbed by Maria's rather matter-of-fact attitude toward life's most precious experience. Maria seemed to be getting just like all the others. Everyone was so practical, as though getting married was some sort of business venture.

They should read her novels and her books of poetry. . . . But perhaps she read too much—that's what the family always said; that was how Hyman always teased her.

"You'll never get a husband, little one," he would say. "A man would be afraid to court you with all your talk of poetry and literature and your philosophizing. There isn't a book or a play you've missed, or a lecture you haven't attended. Men admire scholars, but they don't marry them."

"Becky, don't listen to him," young Ben would counter. "You could have any man in Philadelphia or any place. A real man likes a girl with brains." Ben had never gotten over his baby adoration for his older sister.

"Look who's talking about real men," said Hyman, rumpling Ben's black curls. "Why, you're not dry behind the ears yet; you're just a boy with big ideas."

"I may be a boy," replied Ben, "but I still think Becky is the most wonderful girl I know."

"Hyman. Ben. Stop your silly talk," Rachel scolded; she hated to see them embarrass Rebecca.

"Oh, it's not silly," said Hyman. "I'm serious. If Becky sticks to her books, there won't be a man in Philadelphia that will be her match. One minute she spouts like a historian; the next she is a philosopher. At the drop of a hat, she will offer a commentary or a critique on anything from morals to politics."

"Hush, Hyman. Some man will love her just for that. Not every male is taken by a pretty, empty head." Mama saw Rebecca's eyes filling with tears.

"No, not every male," said Hyman, "but almost every one."

After Hyman and Ben had left them, Rachel turned to Rebecca to offer her some comfort.

"Don't mind Hyman, Becky," she said. "He talks too much."

"He talks too much, but you agree with what he says, don't you?" Rebecca looked at her sister keenly.

"Well . . . I guess I do."

"I thought so. Can't people be just what they are?" Rebecca flung herself into the chair, weeping.

"Of course they can." Rachel patted her shoulder. "It's just that you are a very pretty girl. Men find you attractive but you drive them away. Do as you like . . . read what you like . . . but must you

35

always make a conversation sound like a public forum?"

"You mean I can't talk about anything that is interesting?"

"Of course you can, but try to let the man talk about what interests him. And don't contradict him or turn every little tête-à-tête into a debate. Why, half the time I don't even listen to what Solomon says, I just smile and murmur, 'Isn't that interesting!' or 'Yes, indeedy,' and he's happy."

"Don't you *ever* want to talk to him?"

"About what? Bonnets or recipes? I'm sure he doesn't care any more about that than I do about his business."

"But you're going to be married!" Rebecca could not understand.

"Of course, and Solomon thinks I am very agreeable. He finds me pleasant to be with because I don't argue with him or ruffle his feathers. That is the kind of girl a man likes."

Rebecca was disturbed. This was not what she wanted. She wanted a husband with whom she could share a rare communion of mind and spirit, a companionship that would make her life rich and stimulating.

CHAPTER SIX

1798

THE RIGHT MAN JUST DIDN'T SEEM TO COME ALONG FOR SEVEN-teen-year-old Rebecca.

Rachel was Mrs. Solomon Moses, Frances was Mrs. Reuben Etting, and Richea was Mrs. Samuel Hays. Each one had a fast-growing family and was grateful for Aunt Becky's help. This was especially true of Richea who had settled in Baltimore, far from home. Mama didn't feel well enough to travel, so Rebecca went in her stead. She loved her sister's babies, but she hated being separated from Maria.

These were her thoughts as she arose one morning in Richea's house, hurrying to get down to feed Richea's children, hurrying to do the million and one things Richea could not do because she was still confined to her bed since the birth of her newest little son. Rebecca bathed the baby and wrapped him in his fleecy blankets to bring to his mother; she marveled at his sturdy little frame and the wonderful little hands that clung to her so firmly.

37

"You should be very proud of him," she said as she handed him to Richea.

"Oh, I am. Are the others all right?"

"They're all down at the dining room table having breakfast. And from the sound of the squabbling, they're fine." Rebecca laughed.

"Rebecca, you've been so wonderful to them, and to me. I just love having you here to spoil us all."

"I love being here. It's just that I'm worried about things at home."

"Why?"

"Well, you know the plague is ravaging Philadelphia, and I fear for Mother and Father and everyone."

Richea nodded. "Don't worry, Becky, they'll be all right. We've all survived these things before and, please God, we will this time."

"It's just being so far away and not knowing. . . ."

"Becky, you couldn't do any more there than here. And at least you're safe in Baltimore."

The sound of the doorbell interrupted what Richea was saying.

"Oh, it must be the post," said Rebecca running downstairs and flinging the door open.

"Morning, Ma'am," the man said, handing her a sheaf of letters. "There's one for you in that batch, too."

Rebecca shuffled through the lot until she came to the vellum square that carried her name. It was in Maria's hand. Rebecca tore the envelope open to find just a short note. Her eyes clouded, and she ran back upstairs to Richea.

"Becky, what is it?" asked Richea. "You're so pale."

"Maria . . . her mother and father . . . they're both dead . . . the plague."

"Becky, sit down, sit down. You're shaking."

Rebecca sat in the chair by the bed for a long time. She did not say anything, but just sat with her hands folded. The room reeled

38

"Well, you know the plague is ravaging Philadelphia. . . ."

around her; she did not hear the small cries of the baby or the louder noises of the children downstairs.

"Becky, are you all right?" Richea's voice was soft.

"Yes, I'm all right. Oh, my poor Maria."

"Becky, this is a shock for you and for Maria, but there is nothing anyone can do. That is the horrible part of it all."

It was late that evening before Rebecca could force herself to reply to Maria's sad note. She sat at the desk, pen in hand, trying to find the right words.

> *Dearest Maria,*
>
> My heart aches for you in your time of sorrow. How can anyone know what the loss of parents can mean? If only I could be with you. . . .
>
> But please write and do not restrain yourself from anything you wish to say. After all, listening is a service a friend can render and perhaps it can make your lot more bearable. . . .

This letter marked the beginning of a life-long correspondence and the end of the cozy close-at-hand companionship that had been theirs. Rebecca had to stay in Baltimore longer than she had intended, and Maria had to move to New York to make her home with her brother and his family. From 1800 on, the paths of the two friends were destined to move in different directions.

Rebecca's letters to Maria were frequent; she tried to put on paper every impression, every somberly thought-out conclusion, every honest observation of every day's happenings. She wanted to keep on sharing with Maria as they had always done. She wrote:

> I pray that we can live out our days on the same spot on this earth. After all, we were born about the same time and in the same place. Destiny could not be so cruel as to part us forever.

And if for some reason, we never marry, we will not be unhappy, for we will have the solace of our friendship and the knowledge that we have never been hurt by love's trickery. We would have no complaints and would be happy.

If she read a new book or saw a new play or attended a lecture or a concert, she had to write to Maria, to attempt to share the things they had always shared. Maria's letters, however, seemed to grow more infrequent and more and more preoccupied with beaux and marriage. At times Rebecca grew a bit impatient and even speculated on the prospect of remaining unmarried.

Things were not the same. The two little girls in their rose-sprigged calico dresses, sitting together giggling and whispering, their shining light and dark curls touching, were now a memory, gone as quickly as the fragrant lilacs of spring or the tawny leaves of autumn—gone, leaving behind only nostalgic longing.

But life at 15 Chestnut Street was busy; every moment filled with great activity.

"Never did I think," Michael Gratz would say, "when I was a boy in Silesia that there was some place in the world where a man could make his way to wealth even though he was born in poverty. Never. We should thank God for this America, and we should do whatever we can to sustain such a land."

And every morning as he thanked God for the blessings he had received, he never failed to include a thanks for the bounty that was America and for the good fortune that was his.

After his morning prayers, he and the boys would be off to the general store on Sassafras Street to greet the fur traders and peddlers and land speculators, for Michael Gratz's own holdings extended from fur trading posts in Ohio to Mammoth Cave in Kentucky. In addition, he operated a Kosher meat business in Philadelphia and in the coastal cities.

41

"But, boys," he would say, "business isn't everything. In the Bible it is written that man can not live by bread alone and we must remember this. There is music and art and literature . . . we must never forget. And above all, there is our religion, our great faith in God Almighty."

His children did not forget. They had a wide range of interests. Miriam Gratz, too, was a dedicated woman, never for a moment forgetting those less fortunate than herself and always providing her children with a wonderful example of charitable goodness.

"Rebecca, help me," she would say as she tugged at big bundles of clothing. "These are for that poor Schwartz family that just arrived from Europe. They have nothing. Those poor children will starve if someone doesn't come to their aid." And so she and Rebecca would be off to help the family for whom there was no help. During the eighteenth century, very little was done to provide for the needs of the indigent, the aged, or the orphaned; and the only charity came from the hands of good women like Miriam Gratz.

"Mama," Rebecca said often upon visiting one of these hovels, "it is unbelievable that people can live in such poverty."

"They exist, my child, and what you have seen is only one of hundreds." Miriam Gratz continued with the mending in her hands as she spoke.

"But, Mama, what can we do for them?" Rebecca's tone was disturbed.

"We can only help those near us. It is impossible to help them all."

"But it is so terrible."

"Rebecca, all your buts won't make it less terrible, and while you talk you could be doing something for someone." With that, she placed a bundle of mending in her daughter's hands. "Do what *you* can do, darling, that's all God expects of anyone, and you will feel better just by doing."

By the time Rebecca was in her late teens, she was already hard at work for an organization designed to aid the indigent women and children of Philadelphia. Her efforts were becoming more methodical and more persistent. Every now and then when her aims became grandiose, she would remember her mother's words, "Do what you can do, darling, that's all God expects."

CHAPTER SEVEN

"I Wish You Well"

EVEN DAYS FILLED WITH WORK WERE LONELY. REBECCA HAD many friends, but there was no one like Maria—so warm, so charming, so ready to share the moment and the day. There could never be anyone as dear as her dear friend. So mused Rebecca as she walked in the park one bright September day. The red maples flared like bright flames along the path, mingling their branches with the golden alders. The day was splashed with color.

"If only we never had to grow up," thought Rebecca as she sat on a bench by the path. "We used to have such good times, Maria and I. If we could only spend a few moments together here again, it would be so wonderful!"

Of late, Maria's letters spoke of little except courtship and marriage. There was a Judge Josiah Ogden Hoffman, a widower with several children, who was mentioned most frequently, and a sort of little girl jealousy filled Rebecca's heart. She did not even like the sound of his name. She did not want to share Maria with him or with anyone. Even though she wrote that "the man who will be Maria's husband must be precious to the heart of her Becky," she was uneasy knowing that every day took her old friend further from her.

She had not heard from Maria in over a month, and she could make no more excuses even to herself. She knew that Maria did not find it easy living with her brother, and she knew Maria wanted a way out. But marriage? Marriage should be more than an escape; it should be a glorious adventure. A woman should have someone very special. Two people who cherished the same things could multiply and magnify all the joys of life by the simple act of sharing.

Rebecca did not see the young man strolling down the path, nor did she hear his steps on the gravel path.

"Miss Rebecca?"

She looked up, startled. A tall blond young man stood beside her bench.

"Ah, Mister Ewing! It is Mister Ewing, isn't it? You surprised me."

"I'm sorry. I thought you saw me. You seemed to be looking in my direction."

"I must have been preoccupied staring off into space. I truly didn't see anything."

Rebecca smiled cordially. Samuel Ewing was an old friend of Hyman's. He was the scion of a well-to-do family, his father being provost marshall of the University of Pennsylvania. He himself was a promising young lawyer who had made some additional reputation as a poet.

"Your mother said I would find you here. I told her I had news from Maria Fenno. Your mother was sure you would want word of her before I left Philadelphia."

"Oh, I do. Pray sit down." Rebecca pushed aside her blue organza skirts to make room for him beside her.

45

"Your mother said you were eager for news. Well, to begin with, I saw Maria just three days ago."

"Is she well?"

"Radiant!"

"She hasn't written a word."

"Small wonder. Girls who are just married don't have time for letter-writing."

"Married?" Rebecca could not hide the shock in her voice.

"Oh, I thought she had at least written you the news. All New York is buzzing. Our Maria is the bride of the very honorable Judge Josiah Hoffman. He's been courting her for over a year."

"I knew that," said Rebecca, "but I did not think she would marry him. That is why she has not written. She knew I would not approve."

"Really?" Samuel raised his eyebrows in surprise. "He is a very prominent man, and wealthy. He is what my sister calls a good catch."

"I am sure he is that." Rebecca held her head bowed so that he could not see the tears in her eyes, but much as she tried, the crystal drops rolled down her cheeks.

Samuel reached into his pocket for a clean white handkerchief and gave it to her.

"Please, Miss Rebecca, Maria will be very happy."

"How can she be happy?" asked Rebecca, dabbing the handkerchief at her cheeks. "He is as old as my father. He only wants a mother for his brood."

"And Maria wants a home and a family. We do not all want the same things in life, Miss Rebecca. Be happy that your Maria has what she wants."

"My Maria? She did not even write to me of the most important news in her life."

"Only because she did not want to hurt you. I am sure that is why she sent me."

Rebecca sniffed and tried to smile.

46

"When we were very little girls," she said, "we used to talk about the men we would marry—wonderful and handsome young men, companions with whom we would share our innermost thoughts, our deepest secrets. We wanted a union close and deep. We never spoke of good catches." Samuel listened to this girl as her voice deepened with this poetic avowal of all she held dear, and he was enchanted. She didn't seem real. The rays of autumn sunlight spraying through the trees caught the dark reflections of her hair and made bright prisms of the teardrops caught in her lashes. She was like a princess, lost in enchantment.

"That dream was not Maria's, Miss Rebecca. It was yours, and it still may come true." Samuel touched her hand softly to comfort her.

Rebecca felt the touch and saw the intent look on his face. She blushed prettily and quickly composed herself.

"I did not mean to burden you with my girlish reminiscences, Mister Ewing. I was simply taken aback by your news."

"I am sorry that the news upset you." His voice was soft. "It would never have been my desire to upset you." He rose to leave. "I am on my way back to New York very soon. Do you wish me to give Mrs. Hoffman any message from you?"

"No." Rebecca avoided his steady glance.

"No good wishes?" Samuel waited, hat in hand.

Rebecca still did not answer, seemingly lost in staring at the shadows on the path. Finally she raised her head and smiled.

"I apologize, Mister Ewing, for being so childish. Of course, you must convey my good wishes to the bride. I was piqued at not having been taken into Maria's confidence, but I must not let a lifetime of friendship be wiped out by a slight. Her life must be very full, and I forget I am no longer a part of it. Please tell her I love her and will always pray for her happiness." Rebecca rose also, her blue organza skirts billowing around her.

"May I walk back to the house with you, Miss Rebecca? I am going that way."

47

"Of course, Mister Ewing, I would be most glad of the company. Isn't it a beautiful day? To me there is no season as lovely as autumn with its flamboyant color. It is too lovely to last."

"Lovely," echoed Samuel, oblivious of the season, and the day, and everything, but the girl at his side.

By the time they reached Chestnut Street, Rebecca had almost forgotten Maria.

"Won't you come in and have tea with us?" she asked.

"I can't today. I really have to be on my way back to New York, but I would like to come another time if I may."

"Of course, any time. We'd love having you."

Rebecca's smile lasted as she opened the front hall door. She was almost surprised to see a note in that familiar hand, lying on the hall table. She read:

Dear Becky,

I know I should have written, but a new home and a husband and children do keep me busy. Our home is lovely. I can't wait for you to see it. We were married in such a rush that there was no time for announcements or invitations, and this is the first chance I have had to write.

Please be happy for me. I am content and all is well. I hope you are not offended at not being at my wedding, and I hope Mister Ewing explained everything. Judge Hoffman and I will make it all up to you.

Your loving
Maria

Rebecca stood looking at the note. Could this ill-at-ease document have come from her Maria? Its forced courtesy sounded like the voice of a stranger.

Rebecca went into the library and sat at her father's desk. "I must write something," she thought, and as the pen scratched out the formal words, she tried to forget her own hurt and anger. Not once had Maria said she loved Josiah Hoffman. Not once had she explained why she had so cruelly forgotten Rebecca. Not once had she offered one word more than she had to. But somehow Rebecca had to write; something not angry, not anything; just something to show that she remembered and cherished the friendship they once had. The words were difficult but finally they took shape.

> *Dearest Maria,*
> If I were to say I was not offended by your silence at this time, I would be lying. How many times did we promise we would be witness at each other's wedding? But we were children dreaming children's dreams, and life is not always as we plan it.
> So I must remind myself that the only thing of impor-tance now is your happiness, and I would certainly never want any word or any feeling of mine to flaw what should be your greatest moment.
> I only wish you both well, and pray that the blessings of heaven shine on you and keep you well and con-tent.
> Your affectionate
R G

It was as though Maria had left her to go to some private place where Rebecca could not enter.

CHAPTER EIGHT

$\mathcal{S}amuel$

A FORTNIGHT LATER, SAMUEL EWING WAS BACK IN PHILADELPHIA and, on some pretext or other, back at the Gratz home. The girl he had known only as the younger sister of his friend Hyman had become a very lovely young woman, who excited in him intense feelings of admiration, feelings of a kind he had never felt nor even dreamed possible. Samuel found that Rebecca was not only lovely to look at, but also unbelievably perceptive so that every moment with her was a most agreeable challenge. Rebecca, in her turn, was also excited by the presence of this young man, delighted that she could now tell Maria about this new friend.

"He is here at least once a week," she wrote, "I find him charming, and such a good conversationalist." Someone to talk to—that was so important to Rebecca.

Did Maria recall other words? "I should not want to entrust my happiness to a fool. The companion of our lives should possess qualities to render every situation agreeable, and I think the happiest hours are those passed in social conversation. . . ."

"Rebecca," Samuel would say, "you're the first female who ever made me regard the species as human."

"Samuel Ewing, such intolerance is beneath you. Why, you have written sonnets to lovely ladies, fairly drooling in metaphor."

"True, but that is different."

"Counselor, are you guilty of hypocrisy?"

"With a question like that, I should call *you* counselor. And beware, Miss Rebecca, you are leading the witness who in his simplicity is confused by your wit."

"Methinks the witness would mislead me with semantics," Rebecca laughed, enjoying the parry and thrust of the words. Samuel was entertained, too, and fascinated. More and more he desired the company of this dark-haired enchantress.

The autumn had vanished, and winter had taken its place. Philadelphia rarely saw snow. Instead, a misty dampness spread over the city, over the bare trees and the brown lawns where the brittle corpses of dead leaves lay, moving only when carried by the chill breeze. People made their way through the streets with their heads ducked down into mufflers and greatcoat collars, anxious to find their way to friendly, warm hearths. It was such a day that Samuel entered the Gratz home to find Rebecca seated alone in the library before a snug fire.

"Rebecca?"

"Oh, Samuel. I didn't hear you knock."

"The girl let me in. She said that you were in here. Is Hyman at home?"

"No, not at present, although I expect him shortly. Didn't she tell you that?" She smiled mischievously. Samuel watched her dimple and thought that he had never seen her look so lovely. Scarlet ribbons were braided into her long black hair and wound high around her head. Her frock, too, was scarlet with a ruffling extending from the neck to the hem. From beneath the voluminous skirts peeped two small crimson slippers.

"You look like a winter rose," exclaimed Samuel.

"You talk like a poet," Rebecca laughed.

"Don't laugh, my fine lady, I am a poet, and someday when I am famous, you will be sorry."

"Hyman says that he doesn't know about your poetry, but he thinks you will be a great lawyer."

"Hyman says this, Hyman thinks that. . . . You act as though your brother knows everything."

"I thought that you wanted to see Hyman."

"I do; I want to tell him that he doesn't know everything even though his sister thinks he does."

"Now, about that poetry. . . ." Rebecca's tone was carefully polite and suddenly serious. "It must be fascinating to paint with words the images of your soul."

"You sound like a bard yourself."

"Me? Hardly, but I am a lover of fine writing. The skill escapes me, but I have always felt that so much of the greatness of man lies in his power to express himself and that so much of the wonder of this life lies in the miracle of language that allows us to transmit our thoughts to those around us."

Samuel listened to the gentle voice. All that was real to him was the girl seated in the flickering light of the hearth. The glow of the fire and the softness of the voice intermingled, warming his heart and his mind and driving away all the chill of loneliness that had been his lot for so long.

Suddenly she stopped speaking.

"Please go on," Samuel said, "I was just thinking that Scheherazade must have been much like you."

"Hyman says I talk too much, and I did not want to monopolize the whole conversation."

"Hyman again. I told you that he does not know everything. It is a wonder to find a girl to whom I want to listen. Most of them are too preoccupied with other matters."

"Hyman thinks I am too much preoccupied with the wrong matters."

"Why? Why is he so concerned?" Samuel was indignant.

Rebecca blushed, but she answered, "Hyman says that men do not find women who think attractive."

"Hyman is a fool. Only a fool of a man could want a woman who is a fool. I tell you that men will find you very attractive. In fact, many men find you so now. In fact, Miss Rebecca, that is why I came here today. I did not come to see Hyman," Samuel was blurting out the words. Somehow they did not come out with his usually smooth and urbane manner.

"No?"

"No, I came to ask you to attend the Washington Birthday Ball with me."

"You want me to go with you?" Rebecca's eyes widened. Samuel could have had his choice of any of the belles of Philadelphia.

"Could you please give me an answer or must you consult Hyman?"

"Oh, no—I mean, oh, yes, I would consider it an honor to go with you."

"It is my honor, Miss Rebecca," said Samuel as he gathered up his hat and his great coat and bowed out politely.

A light snow had fallen and he walked through a world transformed by a white-lace veil of flakes; the world was like a bride, a beautiful bride who wore the face of the dark girl he had just left.

CHAPTER NINE

Washington's Birthday Ball

THE NIGHT OF THE BALL ARRIVED AND THE GRATZ HOME WAS aglow with lights. Every room in the house seemed to be in use with someone doing mysterious and urgent errands for Rebecca. Jac and Ben and Richea and Frances had all passed judgment on their sister's gown, and from their unprejudiced point of view, no one could possibly be as lovely as their Becky attired in a heavy white brocade creation. The rich material clung snugly at the waist and then swirled out in huge panniers caught up into festoons and held in place by green velvet roses.

Rachel had fussed and fussed with Rebecca's hair, finally brushing it into one long gleaming curl pulled up high in the back and fastened in place with a dewy white camellia. Small emerald earbobs and an emerald lavaliere completed a picture that the whole family pronounced more than satisfactory.

Mother and Father Gratz would have been happier had Rebecca's escort been David Seixas or Saul Wulf, but they contented themselves with the idea that this night might launch Rebecca into the gay world where they felt young people belonged. Since Maria's marriage, Rebecca had been too withdrawn, too ready to lose herself in philanthropic work. Much as her parents approved of her interest in charity, they worried about this being her exclusive interest. Her little jokes about being an old maid made them uneasy; it was not natural for such a pretty girl.

The mirrors of the huge ballroom reflected the lighted tapers of the chandeliers, creating a glittering fairyland for Rebecca. She catalogued in her mind every gown, every coiffure so that she could make a detailed report to her sisters later. One woman was magnificent in a magenta taffeta, another in scarlet velvet; someone swirled by in a purple bengaline, another bright as a butterfly in tangerine chiffon. Such an array of finery Rebecca had never seen. And the flowers and the jewels and the music. . . .

"Oh, Samuel, what a wonderful evening! Do you have the words to describe these lovely ladies? They're breath-taking!" Rebecca's eyes shone with excitement.

"Peacocks, jays, that's what they are—vain and ugly. They live to preen themselves, occasionally emitting some shrill remark that makes them feel clever."

"Oh no, these women are very beautiful."

"There is only one beautiful woman here tonight, Rebecca. The rest are sham."

"Samuel, you embarrass me." Rebecca's cheeks flushed at his fervor.

"The truth should never embarrass anyone."

"Oh, Samuel, shall we dance?"

They glided along the smooth ballroom floor, the slender dark girl and the fair aristocratic-looking young man, caught up in the tide of music. Her wide overskirts ballooned gracefully as he swung her around and around, and the mirrored walls duplicated the charming scene over and over.

"Oh, look Samuel, there are dozens of us—one in each mirror, all doing the gavotte." Rebecca's voice bubbled happily.

Samuel laughed with her. The gavotte was followed by a minuet and then a waltz. With the perfection of two people who love music and dancing, they whirled gayly to the strains of each melody.

Samuel finally paused, breathless, "Rebecca, may I get you a glass of punch?" He mopped his brow as he looked down at her.

"Oh yes, we had better stop although I hate to lose even one precious moment of the dancing." Her cheeks were rosy, and small tendrils of black hair had escaped their bonds, winding themselves enchantingly on her forehead.

Samuel escorted her to a small anteroom and then went for punch. He returned presently, carrying two glasses. Rebecca sipped hers gratefully.

"My, that is good. Samuel, this evening is completely wonderful. I have never had such a good time. I wish that it would never have to end."

"It doesn't have to, Rebecca. We could spend our lives having wonderful times together." He grasped her hand in his and looked intently into her serious eyes. "I have never known a girl like you, and I never shall. I mean to marry you."

"Samuel, you musn't talk like this." Her eyes were darker now and troubled.

"I must. No woman has ever attracted me. They are all alike—dolls with nothing in their heads but sawdust. To you, I can talk freely of the things in my heart, and you listen with sympathy and understanding. My most cherished ideas are enriched by your just hearing them."

"I know, Samuel you do the same for me. I never knew that such a friendship could exist for a man and a woman. Just knowing you has made me feel less lonely; it also made me realize that I have been lonely all my life. I, too, have found someone in whom I can confide."

"Well?"

Rebecca's eyes filled with tears, but her voice was firm.

"It is not enough. Between us there is a gap that cannot be

. . . they whirled gayly to the strains of each melody.

bridged. I am a Jewess." Every tone in Rebecca's voice was firm.

"Of course you are a Jewess. Your very devotion to your faith gives you dignity few women possess."

"You, too, are sincerely devoted to *your* faith; otherwise you would not be the man you are. That is also part of my respect for you."

"Then, with mutual respect, can we not live together in harmony? Surely we can work out the differences. Others have." Samuel's voice was a plea.

"Others have, but not too successfully. Would my Jewish children regard their father as an outsider? Or would your Christian children have reason to be ashamed of their mother's alien faith? Or would we both grow to hate each other because of ideas that are unchangeable? Our differences would be like cinders in the eye—painful irritations."

"I could change." Samuel's voice was low.

"You could? If you could change, you would not be Samuel. Your greatest virtue is your integrity. Without that, you could be neither a good lawyer nor a good poet. We both live by the Commandmant which says, 'Thou shalt have no gods before Me'—and that means not even love."

"Could you . . . ?" Samuel hesitated.

"Could I give up my religion? You can't even say it, can you? I could as easily give up breathing. My beliefs are my life, my purpose. Without these, I would be a person you would despise. Samuel, I am your friend as you are mine, but marriage for us would be corroded by guilt and recrimination. Neither of us deserves that." Rebecca spoke with finality, her low voice charged with emotion.

"There will never be anyone like you." Samuel bowed his head over her hand and kissed it gently. "Shall I take you home?"

"Yes, perhaps you should." Rebecca rose, hurrying ahead of him out of the room, not wanting him to see the tears that had gathered once again in the dark eyes he loved.

CHAPTER TEN

"Second Best"

FOUR YEARS . . . FIVE YEARS CAN PASS SOMETIMES WITHOUT A PERson being aware that time is passing. Rebecca heard a word about Samuel now and then. Hyman or Jac or Jo would mention his name or pass along some scrap of news, but otherwise that was all. Apparently, no one in the family noted his absence from the Gratz home or at least nothing was said.

It was one afternoon at a charity tea that Rebecca heard of Samuel's forthcoming marriage.

"Is she pretty?" one woman asked.

"A perfect love. Petite and blonde and gentle. His family adores her." The woman distributing the news was a distant cousin of the Ewings.

"I hope Samuel does, too," said Rebecca softly.

"Oh, he does. He dotes on her as one would on a child. He had his family worried for sometime. Seems he had developed an attachment that could have been unfortunate. But thank Heaven, these things pass with young men."

"Yes," said Rebecca. "Thank Heaven, Samuel does deserve a suitable wife."

"Well, I tell you, we never thought it would happen. He was really in love with this girl. He even told his fiancée about it."

"Yes, but, sweet thing, she understood. He said all he could offer was second best."

"That's the poet in him," said Rebecca fearful that her face would betray her emotion.

"Of course, romantic nonsense, he'll forget it all when he settles down."

Samuel did settle down in apparent happiness with his new bride, and yet the memory of his love for Rebecca remained. It was Samuel Ewing's grandchild who was to write the description of the finale of this romance. "Grandfather died at 39 in 1825. My aunt was then ten. She saw Miss Gratz pass into the room where his body lay. When she came out, they all saw that she had left three roses on his breast and her miniature next to his heart. Grandfather had often told Grandmother of his love for Miss Gratz and how a difference in religion had separated them."

CHAPTER ELEVEN

Maria's Daughter

REBECCA HAD RESUMED HER CORRESPONDENCE WITH MARIA Hoffman in New York, and again by letter, the friends discussed the affairs of the day, particularly the problems of Maria's new family. Some of the Hoffman children were almost as old as their young stepmother, but she was as concerned with their welfare as any older, more mature woman might have been.

Mathilda Hoffman was her particular worry. She was frail, delicate, and always a little sickly. When the question of sending her to a school arose, Maria wondered how her stepchild would fare.

"If we could send her where she would be near someone who would check on her now and then, it wouldn't be so bad," Josiah argued.

"There are some fine schools in Philadelphia," said Maria. "And my Becky to watch over her."

"Would this not be an imposition, my dear?"

61

"Not to my Becky. Do you know how much time she gives to charity, to the poor and to the sick, and to children?"

"I know dear, I just meant. . . ."

"Why, Becky's been mothering someone all her life; her brothers, her nieces and nephews. . . ."

"I believe you, dear. I know all about your Becky, and I'll be happy to have our daughter under her watchful eye."

So it was decided to place Mathilda in a finishing school in Philadelphia. Rebecca was delighted to hear of the decision and waited anxiously to welcome the stepdaughter of her girlhood companion.

It was not until late in August of 1809 that she met Mathilda. There was a knock on the door, and Rebecca opened it to find a pretty, slight, blonde girl with a stocky young man at her elbow.

"Miss Gratz?" said the girl.

"Yes."

"I am Mathilda Hoffman."

"Oh, my dear, won't you come in?" Rebecca took Mathilda's hands in her own and drew her into the living room. The young man followed.

"Miss Gratz, I would like you to meet my friend, Mr. Washington Irving."

"Oh yes, this is the young man who works in your father's law office. I am pleased to meet you, Mr. Irving. Mrs. Hoffman has often spoken of you." Rebecca extended her slim white hand to him.

"I am pleased to meet you, also, Ma'am. Mathilda's mother talks of you so much that I feel I know you already." He stood marveling at this striking woman. Certainly she was as old as Mathilda's mother and yet she was so slim and dark. There wasn't a single gray hair in her shining coif.

"Come," Rebecca said, "we can have tea, and you can tell me all the news. How I would love to see your mother!"

In a matter of minutes, the three were chatting like old friends, like people who had known each other well and long. Both Mathilda and Washington felt at ease, warmed by Rebecca's gracious charm. Rebecca, watching them closely, could see how much this fine young man adored Mathilda and also how fragile the girl was.

"I wish I were finished with school," Mathilda was saying. "I hate being away from Mama and Papa and Washington."

"Well, it won't be for long, and we'll try to show you how pleasant Philadelphia can be," Rebecca said.

"And then," Washington chuckled, "I'll swoop back and gather you up and carry you back to my farm in the Catskills. We'll get married and spend the rest of our lives sitting on our stoop while I tell you tall tales. And you'll get fat and rosy and raise a dozen fat and roly-poly children."

Mathilda blushed. "Oh, Washington, how you do go on!"

"Don't you love it?" he said.

"Of course she does," said Rebecca. "Every girl does."

But the pleasant day had to end. Mathilda had to report to her boarding school and Washington had to return to New York.

"Miss Gratz, it's a dreary place," confided Washington to Rebecca. "Watch over her so she won't be too unhappy."

"Of course, of course, she'll be fine," Rebecca promised.

Whenever she could, Rebecca would go out to see Mathilda and take her for a ride in the little open buggy. But even the fresh air did not bring a tinge of pink to the pale cheeks, and the girl seemed to grow more and more listless.

"This can't be lovesickness," said Rebecca, greatly concerned.

"It isn't," said Dr. Hays. "It is consumption."

Rebecca had already moved Mathilda into a bedroom in the Gratz home. Maria was ill, and Judge Hoffman had all he could do to care for the younger children, so Rebecca took upon herself the task of caring for Mathilda.

"Oh, Rebecca, I'm so glad you're here. Please don't leave me."

63

Mathilda's eyes were sunken and glassy, and her hands were thin as claws.

"I won't leave you. You are my Maria's own daughter, and I love you as if you were my own. Sleep, I will sit by you."

Mathilda was beyond all hope. Finally, Judge Hoffman came to take her home to more specialists and to die. Washington Irving was inconsolable. His law career meant nothing. He decided to stay in Philadelphia, making a living doing work for a small newspaper.

"Why don't you write more?" Rebecca would urge him. "It was your love, it could now be your solace."

"It was my love when I could share my thoughts with Mathilda, and make her laugh. Now I have no one and everything is empty."

"Washington, you have everyone and the world needs men like you. It needs your gentle words, your stories to create laughter amid sadness."

"Miss Gratz, Rebecca, I try, but every night when I see her Bible on my desk and know that that little book is all I have left, I weep."

Rebecca tried to console Maria, too, tried to make her appreciate that Mathilda had at least known a wonderful love, that her brief years were not wasted. She wrote:

> *My dear friend,*
> This Washington is a young man such as few girls
> ever know. He gave Mathilda a glimpse of a magic world
> such as few ever see, that is his genius; and she gave him
> a love such as few mortals know. That must be his com-
> fort and yours. It is not how briefly the candle burns,
> but how brightly.

Washington was still drawn to the Gratz home—standing by the fire arguing with Hyman or Jac or Jo, he could forget himself. And if they weren't there, there were others—Doctor Hays or Lawyer Seixas or any of the great or near great of Philadelphia. Papa Gratz's home was famous for its warm hospitality, and it had become a gathering place for all those who sought stimulating companionships. Still, Washington mourned his loss.

"You must write," Rebecca urged. "Only labor you love can heal you."

"You don't know how I feel. You never lost the one you loved." His voice shook.

"Perhaps not this way," said Rebecca, turning away, surprised that tears could still gather at such a long-distant memory.

"Oh, Miss Gratz, I am sorry." Washington had heard the old story about Samuel Ewing, but had forgotten in his own anguish.

"It doesn't matter. It's you that matters. You are making yourself ill; you must make yourself continue to live."

"I don't want to live without Mathilda."

"You have no choice, young man." They turned to see Michael Gratz in the doorway, leaning on his cane. His voice cracked with age and anger. "I, too, would like to be in the grave with my Miriam, but it is not the will of God. In His wisdom, He has given me years and I must live them." The old man stared at the young man. "God has His reasons; you must have faith. You have work that He wants you to do."

Washington did not answer nor did he look up at Michael Gratz.

"Young man," continued Michael, "I do not mean to hurt you more, but you must think of your Mathilda as blessed. She has passed from this earthly travail, and someday when God wills it, you shall join her. In the meantime, try to take consolation in the fact that at least you knew love. That is not a trivial thing, believe me."

The old man sat down in the chair next to Washington, and Rebecca left the room quietly. For over an hour, she could hear the low murmur of voices and hoped that somehow her father had been able to reach out a hand of comfort to her young friend.

When she returned, the two men were sitting quietly, both staring into the fire. Her father looked up as Rebecca entered.

"My child, would you make some coffee for all of us? And also prepare some sort of repast. Mister Irving will be leaving us soon. He has decided to visit with the Hoffmans in New York."

"Yes," said Washington, "your father has convinced me that my presence could be a comfort to them now."

"Oh, it will be, I am sure." Inwardly Rebecca rejoiced, for this was the first time in weeks that the young man had looked outside himself. "You will help each other."

The years passed and Rebecca maintained her interest in Washington Irving, taking personal satisfaction in every work he published. Life could go on, perhaps not always as one had planned, but good, nevertheless, good in the value of achievement. As Papa Gratz said, "God had His reasons; this was the way things were meant to be."

CHAPTER TWELVE

Times Change

THE WORLD WAS CHANGING, AND AMERICA WAS CHANGING, TOO. Napoleon's warlike might was felt in every capital of Europe, and England rallied her forces to try to protect herself against his aggressions. His sale of Louisiana had doubled the size of the United States, making the new country harder to defend. The Napoleonic Wars had brought prosperity to the United States, for every European country was ready to buy its products. But already England blockaded the coasts to try to cut off trade with France; France seized American ships to cut off trade with England.

Philadelphia seemed the same calm city, but here and there merchants and shippers gathered to discuss the latest news.

Hyman was worried. Since Michael Gratz's death, he and Simon had been running the shop on Sassafras Street, and trade was now at a very low ebb. He was lucky to have Jo and Ben to take care of the Kentucky land holdings; otherwise they might have no income on which to subsist.

How times had changed! Papa and Mama were gone—just Rebecca and the four boys left at home. Richea and Rachel were both busy rearing big families in the same traditions their mother had established. Theirs were the children who peopled the house on the holidays, making it gay and happy once more.

Rebecca should have married. Hyman told her this often, and thirty was not too old; he knew many men eager for a good wife.

And how would Rebecca answer his loving tirades?

"Who would care for you, dear brother?" She talked as though Hyman was a little boy. In fact, she talked as though they were all little boys. She cooked and sewed and mended and bossed them, as though she were Mama incarnate; they grumbled, but for the most part did as they were told.

Every Friday night would find the Gratz family in the synagogue. The Congregation Mikveh Israel was the oldest in Philadelphia, and Uncle Bernard had been its president at one time. Hyman was one of the sextons, the *gabaim,* and Rebecca was always so proud as she watched him going through the ritual and chanting the order of the service.

There were so many memories here that were a part of her—the little girl who walked to services with Papa and grew so tired he had to carry her; there was the young lady who had helped at parties and socials, doing everything so efficiently that older women marveled; but most of all, there were the sounds of the chants and the sights of the *Shabbat,* the candle-lighted *menorot,* the old men in their prayer shawls—those old men whose faces were like those of the patriarchs. She could still see her Papa taking the Torah lovingly from the Ark; she could see him shoulder-ing it with pride to bring it to the congregation; she could see him lift his *talit* to his lips and reverently touch the Holy Scroll.

Rebecca could feel herself uplifted with the joys of the Sabbath and her voice rose strong as the congregation sang the closing hymn: *"Adon o-lam asher malach."*

. . . could see him lift his talit to his lips. . . .

Lord of the World, He reigned alone
While yet the universe was naught,
When by His will all things were wrought,
Then first His sov'ren name was known,
And when the all shall cease to be,
In dread lone splendor He shall reign,
He was, He is. He shall remain
In glorious eternity.

The lovely melody rang in her ears as she walked home, her spirit satisfied, her soul at rest.

How could anyone leave this? How could anyone dissever himself from the beauty and the dignity that is Judaism? Rebecca could scarcely understand anyone's desire for conversion, and she was always deeply hurt and disappointed when she heard of any friend or acquaintance drifting from Judaism. How could they?

★   ★   ★   ★

It was 1812 and trouble was in the air. Philadelphia was a seaport, and the reverberations of English and French struggles were beginning to be felt even in its peaceful air. Rebecca worried constantly over what the boys would do; she was glad that her parents had been spared the anguish of seeing the possibility of their sons going to war.

But there was nothing she could do to stop them. Simon was already raising funds and Hyman had set up a business, manufacturing gunpowder. At last it came—the official declaration of war. President Madison asked for volunteers in a fight against England.

"Becky, you don't understand, we have to protect our rights," Jo protested.

"What rights?"

"Our right to the seas."

"When the world's two most powerful nations are in a struggle,

70

little nations should stay away. It is foolhardy for us to think we can gain anything."

"You're the only one who would say a thing like that," said Ben. "You're always so impartial, but you can't be now. This is your country."

"Should I approve of my country and my brothers being fool-hardy?"

"You sound like Papa," Jo and Ben blurted out in unison.

"That's the nicest thing you could have said."

"But we have to protect our western frontier from the Indians. General Jackson says so," continued Ben.

"And who will protect the Indians from General Jackson?" queried Rebecca with a wry smile.

"Why should they be protected?" asked Jo.

"Shouldn't everyone?" said Rebecca. "Don't they have rights?"

"But the British are inciting them," said Ben.

"I know, I know, the white man will eventually destroy them," said Rebecca.

"Becky, you just don't want to understand, do you? But we have to tell you; Jo and I want to enlist." Ben's tone was firm, but his eyes were down, concentrating on his knotted fingers.

"Haven't you already enlisted?" Rebecca's gaze was steady.

"How did you know?" Again the brothers spoke in unison.

"Because I've known you both since you were born, and you've never been good liars." She smiled through her tears. "I love you both, and I hate to see you go, but I wish you Godspeed and a safe return."

She enfolded Ben's head in her arms and kissed his dark curls.

"Take care. Both of you, take care."

"We will, Becky, don't worry," said Jo.

"Oh, I won't worry," said Becky, wiping away the tears and managing a smile. "I won't worry for anyone except the English and the Indians."

★ ★ ★ ★

71

And so Ben and Jo were off to the wars; Becky wrote faithfully, instructing them to send their laundry home. She baked honey cakes, packaging them in tins; she knitted sweaters; she prayed. Her every thought was occupied with their concern.

She wrote to Ben regularly and worried because he was her baby; the same toddler who had followed in her footsteps and who had been her complete charge when Mother was away or ill.

> *My dear Ben,*
> Every day I pray for your speedy and safe return. We are lost without you and Jo, and we look forward to every letter. Is there any possibility of your getting a leave? We would love seeing our soldier.
> I worry lest you try to be too much of a hero. Even the thought of your going into battle fills me with fright. You must be patient with my sentiments, for after all, I am a mere woman.
> If God wills it, there will be a speedy armistice to bring you safely home.
>> Your affectionate
>> *R G*

Ben was being moved farther into Kentucky; the Gratz family had had holdings there since 1774. As mile after mile intruded between them, Rebecca began to be plagued with premonitions that Ben would never return home.

"If he stays in Kentucky, he will miss all the culture Philadelphia has to offer," she confided to Hyman.

"Who knows, Becky?" Hyman said. "Perhaps Kentucky has other things to offer a young man. It's a new country with new opportunities. He might even do something with our land holdings there."

"But it's a wilderness."

"Philadelphia was wilderness once, too."

"But Ben is no pioneer. He likes pretty girls and the theater and. . . ."

"There are plenty of pretty girls in Kentucky, I'm sure."

"I'm sure there are no pretty *Jewish* girls."

"Ah-ha, now the truth is out. You're worried about whom Ben will meet." Hyman's eyes met Rebecca's, and they both laughed.

"Don't worry, Sister," he continued, "you've spoiled him thoroughly. With the coddling he gets in this house, he'll never leave. He'll probably come home and join the bachelor group with me."

"It's about time you began to think of. . . ." Rebecca began.

"I know, I know. I'm thinking." Hyman grabbed his hat and made for the door. He knew that his sister was about to embark on her usual tirade concerning his finding a wife and settling down, and his situation suited him too well to even listen.

Ben had met someone in Kentucky, a very charming someone named Maria Gist. Maria's bright eyes and sweet smile drew him to her. She was like Becky, always ready to talk about books and music and art. Her company pleased him like few others he had known. She reminded him somehow of his beloved sister, Rebecca.

The Gist family, too, was like his, interested in politics and in their community. They had been associated from the first with the Revolution and with George Washington. There was even a family legend that the great general's first love was one of Maria's lovely ancestors. He knew that Rebecca would admire the Gists and Maria as much as he; but he also knew she could not approve of the step he contemplated.

He meant to marry Maria, and he knew how Rebecca would feel. He knew what she thought of marriages between Jews and Gentiles. It was with great care that he worded his letter to her, and it was with great shock that Rebecca read what he had written.

"Hyman, I can't believe it," she said over and over. "I want him

73

to be happy. I pray that he will be happy, but this girl is not for him."

"Becky, he's not your baby any more. He has to make up his own mind."

But Rebecca could not get her brother out of her mind. As she sat down to compose a letter to him, thoughts kept flashing through her mind—of Ben, curly haired Ben, the little boy she had read to and played games with, whose face she had washed, and whose hurts she had tended. How could she let him hurt himself now? He had always been so devout; his religion had meant so much to him.

It was from her heartache that the words came:

Dear Ben,
You know that I would wish you no harm and that I pray ever for your happiness. With these thoughts in mind, I beg you to reconsider your decision.

You know of many instances of such marriages. Aunt Shinah's was one. And you know they are not all that is to be desired. In youth, we are attracted by beauty; we feel the need for a companion, but often we are betrayed by desire.

It is then that we sacrifice ourselves and our beliefs for momentary pleasure.

I am sure that your Maria is all you say she is; you could love no one who was less. And for these reasons, I beg you not to show her this letter.

I have no desire to hurt her; all I hope for is to enlighten you and to keep you from making a step you could regret.

Your devoted
R G

But nothing Rebecca could say would deter Ben. His mind was made up. Hyman had little wish to discuss the matter further, so it

74

was to friend Maria that she turned, pouring her thoughts into another letter.

> . . . I have ever tried to be of an open mind. Most of my friends are of a different faith but I have never loved one less on that account, and I hope that they have not withheld their affection from me.
>
> But in family life, I feel that a mother and a father should share the same devotion, so that they will be able to give their children some sense of tradition and some sense of their true relationship to God. If there is no true union of belief between husband and wife, how can this ever be?
>
> It is for this reason I do not approve of Ben's marriage to Maria Gist. Certainly her family and she are all anyone could desire, but I am not ambitious in this respect. I want neither wealth nor prestige for my brother, only happiness, the kind of happiness my parents knew.

CHAPTER THIRTEEN

Benjamin

REBECCA'S FEARS SOON BECAME FACT. THE ARMISTICE WHICH she welcomed brought peace but did not bring Ben home. He married Maria Gist and settled down in Kentucky. There, he was to live out his life far from his beloved sister, Rebecca.

"Hyman, it doesn't seem possible."

"What, Becky?"

"That I can go into the library and not find Ben hard at work."

"You miss him, don't you?"

"I try not to."

"Have you written?"

"Not since the wedding. I sent our gift, but that was all."

"You will write, though, won't you?"

"Of course. I bear neither of them ill."

Hyman did not look up from his newspaper.

"I think," he said, "it's time you stopped mourning."

Rebecca's mind thought back to that day so long ago when they had all found out about Aunt Shinah, how Mama and Grandpa had mourned as though Shinah was dead, how she and Ben had felt.

"Oh, no," she said, "I am not doing that."

"Then, write that letter."

Rebecca did not answer Hyman, but she walked steadily to the library. She sat down at the same desk where she was so used to seeing Ben and took her quill in hand. To her surprise, the words flowed easily from her pen.

My dear Maria,
The time has passed for any feelings of doubt or fear. You are now my sister, entitled to all the love and affection that goes with that position. You are the wife of my beloved brother and I know you will give him lifelong happiness. I am sorry he showed you my letter. I did sincerely admonish him not to, since my frankness was only for his eyes. My opinions were not due to any disrespect for you or your family, and I would not hurt you in any way. I merely tried to bring to his mind factors which I thought might cause you both regret. But now we are all one family and we must devote ourselves to each other and not to our differences.

Yours affectionately,
R G

She did not press Maria to raise the children in the ways of Judaism.

"This is a matter for their own conscience," she told Hyman. "I would not want to be the reason for discord. A divided family is no family." She took pleasure in the fact that Maria was a wonderful mother and a good wife, and corresponded with her frequently on the matters near and dear to each of them. Rebecca often explained her feelings for Judaism at great length.

Hyman laughed one day as he read a few lines over her shoulder.

"You aren't trying to convert our sister-in-law, are you, Becky?"

"Hyman! Of course not! I simply think I can help her understand our ways. I respect her creed and hope she can respect mine."

"And Ben's?"

"Hyman, you are too clever, you see through me completely."

Rebecca was happy that Ben was happy but she wondered if anything could make up to her brother for not having a small hand to hold in his at synagogue as he had done with Papa; for not having a small voice shyly pipe the four questions at the seder table; for not being able to see his sons called up to the Torah; for not having anyone to say kaddish for him when he died.

"How can I do anything but make the best of such a union?" Rebecca asked herself again and again. "One cannot discard one's Jewishness as one throws off an old garment. It is too much a part of us." Rebecca's instincts were very deeply rooted, far stronger than any intellectual argument. She remained close to Benjamin and his Maria throughout their lives, but she never ceased to mourn the loss of his children to Judaism.

The words of Michael Gratz echoed in her memory. "It is through our children that we keep our covenant with our God." For Ben, this was not meant to be.

CHAPTER FOURTEEN

A Kentucky Friend

IT WAS THE FIRST MORNING OF REBECCA'S RETURN FROM LEXING-
ton, Kentucky, where she had been visiting Ben. She was up early
and had warm muffins and hot coffee on the table when Jo and
Hyman came downstairs.

"Well, Jo, this is more like it!" Hyman smiled as he sat down at
his place, unfolding his napkin.

"It certainly is," said Jo. "Becky, as soon as I smelled that coffee,
I knew you were home."

"You two don't look well. Jo, you look tired. Hyman, you're
getting gray." Rebecca frowned at them both.

"Rebecca, we're only three weeks older than we were when you
left. It's just that we don't do well without you." Hyman leaned
across the table to kiss Rebecca's cheek.

She touched her fingers to his cheek. "I missed you," she said.

"I missed you, too."

"And me?" said Jo.

"Of course, Jo. I missed you."

For a moment, the three sat silent. Sometimes, it is sad to love, and this was a moment of sadness.

"Come now, enough of that," said Hyman. "How is our Ben?"

"He's fine and Maria's fine and the children are wonderful."

"And what is our baby brother doing?" said Jo, patting strawberry jam on his muffin.

"Well, his law practice is flourishing and he has so many friends. I met a great many and they all speak so well of him."

"To his sister, what would people say?" teased Hyman.

"Never mind—to his sister. He has just been elected to the city council, and he has just been asked to be a trustee of Transylvania University."

"Our little brother does do well, Hyman," said Jo.

"Very well," said Rebecca emphatically.

"And did they treat you well, Sister?" asked Hyman.

"Indeed. Maria had a party in my honor, and Henry Clay himself was one of the guests."

"What is he like?" said Hyman, leaning forward in interest.

"Very like what the papers say—big and sandy-haired and very well-spoken. He could charm the birds off the trees. Ben says he should be our next president."

"Perhaps, although I've heard it said he's an anti-Semite," said Jo.

"It's not true," Rebecca protested. "Why, Ben is *his* best friend. They are always together. Ben and I drove to his place in Ashland, and we were made more than welcome."

"It sounds as though you had a good visit," said Jo.

"I did," said Rebecca, "but now I miss them all the more. I do wish Ben had stayed in Philadelphia."

"And Maria?" said Hyman.

"She is lovely; she truly is," said Rebecca.

"But?" said Jo.

"But she is Gentile, and so are the children. I love them, but the fact remains a fact."

Rebecca sighed. Ben was doing well in Kentucky with a career that promised to grow greater. He was one of the directors of the first railroad in the West and organizer of the first bank in Kentucky, and additionally, he was a friend of the great Henry Clay. Ben's razor-keen mind was a perfect sounding board for the great man's political ideas and theories. Ben had been one of the youngest lawyers to pass the bar in Pennsylvania, and he could offer the older man the kind of constructive criticism every man in public office cherishes.

Rebecca learned more and more of Clay through Ben and Maria's letters, and she began to follow his career with intense interest.

How unusual, she thought, for this man and her brother to be so close. She had heard that Clay's domestic life was unhappy; just what was wrong, Ben never said, and she felt sure that Ben's, too, must be lacking. How could he not at times feel quiet remorse or regret? Was that not a natural thing in all marriages? "Perhaps," she thought, "this unhappiness caused them to direct so much of their effort outside their own domiciles."

"Your brother talks of nothing but you," Clay had said when he met Rebecca, clasping her hands warmly.

"To me, he talks of little but you, Mister Clay," Rebecca answered.

She could see why this man was so effective as "The Great Compromiser." In seconds, he had put her at ease, his genial good nature enveloping all her doubts and prejudices against politicians.

"That's because he's the real thing, Becky," Ben assured her. "He's a great man and a great statesman, and he loves people as much as he appears to."

Rebecca nodded. Ben's loyalty was just as she remembered it—flawless and unswerving.

Once during a campaign, Clay inadvertently made a remark about "Moses Myers, the Jew" and immediately was branded an anti-Semite by many. Rebecca read the speech through carefully without being able to make any sense out of the allusion. "Ask Mr. Clay if he can explain," she wrote to Maria. Myers was such a harmless old man that an attack on him seemed senseless. Clay's response was immediate. In a public statement, he made clear his feelings for the Jewish people, pointing with pride to his long association and friendship with Benjamin Gratz.

It was in 1848 that Henry Clay failed to get the presidential nomination, and the whole Gratz family was disappointed. Rebecca consoled Ben, reminding him that Clay might be destined for greater things.

But by 1852, Henry Clay was dead. He died as he had lived, loved by many, respected by many, but still alone. As his strength ebbed, he lay in his bed in his Washington hotel room, tended by strangers, far from the invalid wife who was too helpless to come to him.

Benjamin Gratz was a part of the committee who arranged to bring Clay's body home to Kentucky. Rebecca grieved for the man, even though he was a comparative stranger. She wrote to her niece saying:

> Ah, how poor a thing is greatness and fame. Here is a man, honored by his country, who in his dying hour had not one familiar voice to ease his pain, not a familiar hand to touch his brow. This is indeed sadness.

CHAPTER FIFTEEN

"Is Rebecca You?"

REBECCA FOLLOWED WASHINGTON IRVING'S CAREER WITH GREAT interest. Always an avid reader, she grasped every one of his books as it appeared, devouring every line, catching for a moment something of his wonderful presence. It had been over six years since Irving had been in America; his travels had taken him far away. He had spent most of his time in Spain, but he had also toured France and England. It was during his stay in England that he made a pilgrimage to the home of the great novelist, Sir Walter Scott.

Scott was another of Rebecca's favorites. His tales of historical adventure fascinated her. It was in April of 1804 that she read his newest work, a medieval romance entitled *Ivanhoe*.

She read with rare excitement. This was a tale, unusual for an author of that time, because its heroine was a Jewess also named

Rebecca. This girl, daughter of Isaac of York, was exceptionally beautiful, even for a romantic heroine. In the words of Sir Walter Scott, "The figure of Rebecca might indeed be compared to the proudest beauties of England . . . her form was exquisitely symmetrical, and was shewn to advantage by a sort of Eastern dress . . . her turban of yellow silk well-suited to the darkness of her complexion. The brilliancy of her eyes, the superb arch of her eyebrows, her well-formed aquiline nose, her teeth white as pearl, and the profusion of her sable tresses, which each arranged in its own spiral of twisted curls, fell down upon as much of a lovely neck and bosom as a simarre of rich Persian silk, exhibiting flowers in their natural color on a purple ground, permitted to be visible . . . all these constituted a combination of loveliness, which yielded not to the most beautiful of maidens who surrounded her."

Rebecca could not put the book down. This heroine who was her namesake came alive amid the pageantry of the days of knighthood. This fictional Rebecca was all fire and courage, resisting the romantic efforts of Bois Gilbert even though it could mean her life, spurning him not only because he was evil but also because he was Christian. Rebecca's rescuer was the handsome hero, Wilfred of Ivanhoe—tall, blond, and brave, willing to risk his life in combat for this *girl* so wrongfully accused. Naturally, as in all romances, the hero saved Rebecca's life. But then came a strange turn of events—Rebecca went out of his life because she was a Jewess and he a Christian.

The novel was well received everywhere. People were immensely attracted to the character of the lovely Jewess and protested that Scott should have allowed Rebecca and Ivanhoe to marry. She was so real that many readers felt quite strongly on the matter. Scott felt called upon to reply. Invariably, he gave the same answer to all. "Such a union," he said, "would have been inconceivable in the Middle Ages due to the prejudices of the period." In addition, such an arrangement would have been out of keeping with a character of such a "highly virtuous and lofty

84

stamp." He also maintained that his fictional Rebecca's high-minded discharge of duty brought her "more adequate recompense, in the form of peace, which the world cannot give or take away."

Rebecca loved the novel, writing about it with great enthusiasm to her sister-in-law, Maria, advising her to read it if she had not already done so. In her opinion, the fictional Rebecca was a paragon of virtue, one whose faith was even stronger than the temptation of her own desires.

When the nieces and nephews read Scott's tale, they could not help but see the heroine's resemblance to their beloved Aunt Becky.

"Is Rebecca you, Aunt Becky?" they would ask, but Rebecca never did more than shrug. It was a pleasant idea, but who could know? The legend grew in the family and in the folklore of literature but no real proof could be found.

Interesting, indeed, is the description of Rebecca by the renowned portrait painter, Thomas Sully, a young genius introduced to the Gratzes by Washington Irving. From his notebook comes a description of the real Rebecca: "Never seen a more striking Hebraic face. The easy pose, suggestive of perfect health, the delicately turned neck and shoulders with the firmly poised head and its profusion of dark curling hair, large clear black eyes, the contour of the face, the fine white skin, the expressive mouth and the firmly chiseled nose, with its strength of character, left no doubt as to the race from which she had sprung. Possessed of elegant bearing, a melodiously sympathetic voice, a simple and frank and gracious womanliness, there was about Rebecca Gratz all that a princess of Blood Royal would have coveted."

The similarity between Scott's fictional Rebecca and Sully's real Rebecca adds only another interesting footnote to the tale.

CHAPTER SIXTEEN

Facing Disaster

SOON I'LL BE FORTY YEARS OLD, THOUGHT REBECCA, AS SHE LOOKED into her mirror. There were no gray hairs, though, and only a few lines near the eyes. She straightened the white collar on her black dress and pinned a small watch to the bodice of her long blue pinafore.

She looked down at the watch. It was almost nine. Time to be off to the orphanage. There was always so much to do, she hated to be late. There were letters to be written, money to be raised, food and fuel to be solicited, and more important there were faces to be washed, stories to be read, and sticky little hands to be held.

The non-sectarian Philadelphia Orphan Society was a big part of Rebecca's life, and she had played an important role in its growth. The Gratz home on Chestnut Street was always filled with influential people, and Rebecca was never too proud to ask for help for her orphaned babies—bedding, fuel, food, clothing, medicine, time; anything that could be given would be gratefully received. The greatest and most desperate need for the children was a new home, but so far, that was a dream. The ladies had all they could do to make ends meet.

The old house in which the children were quartered was a nightmare for Rebecca. It was as clean as hands could make it but it was ancient and ramshackle and far from safe.

One frigid night, in December of 1821, disaster struck.

"Fire . . . at the orphanage," a messenger blurted out as Rebecca answered the frantic knocking at the door.

"Oh, no . . . please God . . . no." Rebecca threw her cloak round her shoulders and ran through the streets toward the orphanage. The building was a blazing horror! The fire brigades could do little to save the pitiful place her waifs called home. Twenty-two precious lives were snuffed out quickly in the enveloping smoke.

Dry-eyed, Rebecca and the few women who constituted the directorate, shepherded the rest of the children into a small lonely group.

"Miss Gratz, may I help?" said a voice from the crowd. It was old Mrs. Moses; she was leaning on her cane, trying to make her way through the crowd.

"Oh, Mrs. Moses," said Rebecca. "You are an angel. Do you have a bed for this little boy for tonight?" She put her hand on one seven-year-old tot's curls. He was shivering in the cold.

Mrs. Moses enfolded him in her shawl.

"Of course I do. I can take two or three if you'll trust an old woman."

Rebecca's eyes filled with tears.

"God bless you," she said kissing the wrinkled old cheek. She watched the crowd part for the old woman and the three tots Rebecca assigned to her.

"Miss Gratz, I'll take this one. We'll make room for her with our brood." It was Mr. Alexander, the butcher, who had ten chil-

"Fire . . . at the orphanage". . . .

dren of his own. He had already encased a small freckle-faced girl in his greatcoat and was making off with her in his arms.

"I know a big house with room for three or four," said another big voice. It was Hyman followed by Jo and Jac.

"Oh, boys, I am so glad to see you. Can you manage until I get home to help?"

"Becky, we've been uncles for years. Jo, you put them in the wagon, and get them home to bed. I'll stay and help." Hyman tucked a child under each arm and made his way to the wagon. Jo followed, similarly burdened.

"We were just getting back from a delivery when we heard. We got here as soon as we could," said Hyman.

"You were never more welcome, Mr. Gratz," said one of the ladies.

"All right, now, let's get busy." Hyman clapped his hands together, ready for work.

One by one, the children were parcelled out, at least for the night.

"Oh, Hyman, whatever will we do?" Rebecca looked at the charred skeleton of a building, now a smouldering ruin.

"I don't know," he said, "but we'll think of something. Come, let's get home and get you to bed. You look exhausted."

Together they walked home. A light snow was falling, and the air was chilly. Neither brother nor sister said a word; their fatigue was too overwhelming.

Jo opened the door for them.

"Come, Cook left you coffee. It will do you good."

"Are the children all right?" said Rebecca.

"Fine. Cook washed every hand and face and put them all to bed."

"Did she find night clothes for them?"

"She used some of my flannel nightshirts and some of Hyman's."

"Poor little tykes," groaned Hyman, "they must be swimming in them."

89

"They were big, but we rolled up the sleeves, and they're warm and comfortable."

"We'll get them clothes in the morning," said Rebecca. "There must even be a few things around from Richea's or Rachel's children. I can even look now."

"Not now, Becky," said Hyman. "Tomorrow will do. How about that coffee? It sounds good to me."

"No, I don't think so," said Rebecca. "I think I just want to sit down for a few moments before I get ready for bed."

She walked into the library and sank down into the big chair. She could smell the acrid odor of smoke that still clung to her clothing and her hair. Suddenly, the tears began to flow, and she did not try to stop them. She sat, mourning each and every small life that had been lost that horrible night.

As the tears streamed down her cheeks, she began to repeat the words of the *kaddish,* the prayer for the dead:

"Magnified and sanctified be His great name in the world which He hath created according to His will. May He establish His kingdom during your life and during your days and during the life of all the house of Israel, even speedily and at a near time, and say ye, Amen."

Somehow there was comfort in the ancient words, and as she leaned her head back against the chair, she slept.

Hyman found her there in the morning.

"Becky, were you here all night?"

"I must have been."

"Well, you get up to your bed and get an hour's rest."

"I can't. I can't. There's too much to do."

"I know, Becky, and I'll help you. But you must rest."

"No, I must see Mr. Brown about an article for the newspaper. We must start a building drive at once. And you see Mr. Bronson and Mr. Sidney at the bank. There's a building on Market Street they want to sell. I thought of it last night."

Hyman managed a smile.

90

"Could we do these things after breakfast?"

"Of course, of course. I'll just go upstairs and freshen up and then be down to join you. We'll be having our guests with us for a while."

"I know. Two are in my bed." Hyman smiled indulgently.

"Where did you sleep last night?"

"On the couch in the living room."

Rebecca laughed. "You didn't. How did you fit?"

"It wasn't easy, but I'm acrobatic. This morning I feel like a pretzel. A few days of this and I'll be a petrified pretzel."

Rebecca's face grew serious.

"You don't mind, do you, Hyman? They have no place to go."

"No place? Now you're adding insult to injury. Since when is our home no place?"

Rebecca brightened.

"You're a wonderful man, Hyman."

"And you're a wonderful lady, Becky. Haven't I ever told you?"

Still smiling, Rebecca hurried upstairs, her mind a jumble of ideas and plans. Today was a new day with work to be done.

CHAPTER SEVENTEEN

Add Nine

IT TOOK TIME AND EFFORT, BUT BY SOME MAGIC THE LADIES TOOK that house on Market Street until a new orphanage could be built. Money poured in from all over the state, even from Ben's friends in Kentucky, where his wife had founded an orphan society.

"Poor little souls," Rebecca would say. "They need help so desperately."

Hyman looked at his sister, the bookish girl. The sweet and carefree ways of the debutante were gone, in their place was a dedicated woman—cultured, kind, eager to be of service in any way she could.

"Perhaps," she said, "these children were meant to be my family, since God saw fit to give me no children of my own."

The orphan society was non-sectarian, and so to Jew and Gentile child alike, Rebecca gave unswerving devotion.

Rebecca's services to the Gentile community had always been readily accepted, particularly her work with the orphans. Jewish philanthropy was in its infancy because the Jewish community itself was new. As immigration increased, the problems of the Jewish community grew, and it was only natural for Rebecca to take the experience she had garnered and bring it back to her own people. No demand on her time or her efforts was too great, but never did she forget her own family.

"Becky, you're wonderful," said Rachel. "Here you have fifty children of your own and you still have time for mine."

"Am I not a maiden aunt? And is that not what we are for? To help our married sisters who should have had better sense."

Rachel laughed.

"Becky, you should have married. You're wonderful with children."

"Rachel, I can handle my fifty orphans better than your brood. They're so lively, and so spoiled."

Rachel laughed. The Moses children now numbered nine, and Rebecca was a godsend, always willing to help.

"They're wonderful. I wish I had a dozen more," Rachel laughed, patting Sara's curls and kissing Simon's nose.

"You probably will at this rate, and I will quit—completely worn out. You are a natural-born mother, my Rachel. No one is like you."

"All women are, Sister. Aren't you? Actually you have more children than I." The two sisters would laugh. Nothing could ever destroy such happiness, Rebecca thought.

But in September of 1823, a yellow fever epidemic struck, claiming Rachel and the newest baby as victims. Solomon Moses was desperate.

"Rebecca," he said. "I'm never home. My business keeps me away weeks at a time. Who will care for my children?"

93

"Solomon, don't worry. I'm here." Rebecca put her hand on his shoulder.

"But you can't stay. You have the house and boys in Philadelphia."

"Then I'll take them all home to Philadelphia with me."

"That would help temporarily."

"Temporarily? Don't talk nonsense. I'll keep the children as long as they need me."

"Rebecca, you don't know what you're saying. You're a young woman, you should have a life of your own."

"Solomon, I'm forty-two years old. I have no intention of marrying if that is what you're worried about. Men my age want young girls . . . and older men are crochety. My brothers are living examples of that."

"But Becky. . . ."

"Don't 'but Becky' me, it's all arranged. Solomon, it's God's will. He meant me to be here to help you. Perhaps it is His will that Rachel's children should be my life. Is that so very bad?"

Solomon kissed her gently.

"You're a good woman, Becky. How can I ever repay you?"

"By helping us pack. It'll take a wagon just to take your children's toys to Philadelphia."

★　★　★　★

Once again the house on Chestnut Street was filled with the sights and sounds of children.

"Ssh, children, Uncle Hyman is napping," Rebecca would say.

"Rebecca, you must be joking. How could anyone nap in this bedlam?" Hyman would bellow.

"Well, as long as you don't intend to nap, would you take Horace for a walk in the park?"

"Of course," Hyman managed a wry smile. "That's the real reason I came home from the turmoil of my office."

But Rebecca was not even listening. She was too busy bundling Horace into his overcoat and churning over in her mind the details of running a household for children ranging in age from three to sixteen.

The days after Rachel's death had been filled with such silence and brooding that now the sounds of banging doors and running feet were a welcome relief. The sight of those motherless bairns clothed in sombre black, sitting passive and unsmiling at each meal had almost broken Rebecca's heart. Every day she said prayers to God for strength and wisdom to help them.

"These children are my greatest concern," she wrote to Maria. "They have given me a reason for living, and each day is now filled with love and purpose, the like of which I have never known."

Dropped mittens, measles, squabbles . . . all this Rebecca was prepared to cope with. But how do you mend the heart of a child mourning his mother?

Each one mourned in his own way. Isaac, the eldest, was tearless, but Rebecca could see his hands shake as he sat at the table trying to eat.

Rebecca knew that in his sixteen-year-old way, he was trying to be an example to the others. She knew that at night he buried his head in his pillow and sobbed so that the others would not hear. She could hear him tossing and turning in the darkness long after the little ones were asleep. She would call his name, but he would not answer, and she knew that he had to be alone with his own sadness.

How could she comfort them . . . give the help Rachel would have given . . . safeguard them from dangers as Rachel would have done . . . guide them as Rachel would want them to be led?

"Please God, help me," she prayed. "There is no love more perfect than a mother's, but help me to give them what they need."

How could she explain their loss to them? She must try. As she searched her own heart, she knew she must teach them that God is good—that all of His acts are part of His wisdom and His mercy. She knew now where her own strength came from. These were the teachings of her own mother and father; this was their constant example of piety and goodness. Life with all its pain and suffering was a pattern, sometimes only made bearable by one's faith in God, but from that faith, she knew that they would all be able to go on.

The little ones she could cuddle. The warmth of her body and a soft lullaby were all that Horace needed to drift off to dreams, his three-year-old face streaked with tears and his chubby little hand holding tight to hers. Horace was her darling; he needed her most, and she needed him, too.

To each child, Rebecca gave herself in a different way, and each gave her a different sort of appreciation.

"Look at the girls," she said to Hyman. "They're growing in front of our eyes, and they are so pretty."

"And so vain," he grumbled. "All I find all over the house are ribbons and combs."

"It's their age," said Rebecca. "They can't believe it themselves that they're growing up."

"They look in the mirror often enough to believe it. And Becky, I meant to speak to you, do you know what those last two ball gowns cost?"

"I've forgotten," Rebecca said innocently.

"It was a great deal."

"Some things are more important than money."

"But we can't afford. . . ."

"We can't afford not to. The only time a girl can enjoy a pretty gown is when she's young."

Hyman shrugged. Talking seemed to do no good. Rebecca was suddenly reliving her own girlhood. Watching the girls fuss over their finery reminded her of the time in her life when a new gown was reason for ecstatic excitement. Their performances reminded her of pleasant days, days filled with long-forgotten fragrance and melody; and for fleeting moments the past came back to her—a welcome gift, a beautiful echo. The girls were not all vanity; they tried to be useful and helpful, and Rebecca knew the time would come when they would have to settle down just as she had.

* * * *

Actually, this was the first time Hyman had ever mentioned economy. Money had just never been important. The business established by Papa Gratz and his brother, Bernard, had always gone so well that Rebecca never even thought about money or the lack of it.

Papa and Uncle Bernard had grown rich in the fur trade. Their boats had plied the Ohio and the Wabash. Hyman, Simon, Jo, and Jac had stayed in the business expanding it still further. But now something was wrong.

"Hyman, why can't you talk about it?"

"Becky, I try, but you just don't understand business. We just overextended ourselves and we can't pay our creditors."

"But why?"

"Why? Who knows why? I can blame Simon and he can blame me or Jo can blame Jac . . . it's just bad luck, that's all." Hyman put his head in his hands. "I just don't know what to do."

"Do? We'll start again, that's all." Rebecca smiled with perfect confidence. "Your reputation must be worth something."

"Becky, you're like a child. You just don't understand."

"All right, so I don't. But you'll see."

"You'll see when we have to move. . . ."

"Move? From this house?" Rebecca looked around the room she had known since childhood. In every nook and cranny was a memory. Her face grew serious.

"Yes, move. I didn't want to tell you this way." Hyman looked pained.

"What way could you tell me? It's as bad for you as it is for me."

Rebecca picked up the sock she had been darning and stitched methodically. "When do we move?"

"As soon as possible." It was Jac's voice in the doorway. "We should have told you before, Becky, but you were so busy with the children."

"You should have told me. I would have been more careful about spending money." Rebecca looked at Hyman.

"Becky, a few dollars more or less at this point doesn't mean a thing."

The three sat, the two men staring into the fire and Rebecca absorbed in her mending. There was a step in the hall and they looked up. It was Simon.

How old he looks, thought Rebecca, and how weary! Nothing matters this much; nothing should do this to a man. He sat down heavily in a chair.

"Can I get you something, Simon?" Rebecca asked.

"No, nothing, I just want to rest a minute before I tell you the news." He mopped his brow.

"More bad news," said Hyman. "You don't have to bother."

"No, this time it's good." Simon smiled through his weariness. "You know Mr. Elkin. . . ."

"Of course, he's a creditor," snapped Jo.

"Well, he was in. . . ."

"Couldn't he wait? We're not going into bankruptcy?" Jac said. "Is he afraid he'd be cheated?"

"Jo, Jac . . . let me say something! Let me tell you."

"All right, Simon, tell away," said Hyman. "We'll listen." He held a silencing finger to his lips for Jo's and Jac's benefit.

"He came in and said he would tear up any notes we owed him; that we could take ten years to pay him if we liked."

"He did?" This time Hyman interrupted in surprise.

"Yes. And he said he'd go to the bank and sign more notes for us. It's unbelievable." Simon took out his handkerchief to wipe his eyes. He blew his nose hard.

"He says he does it out of respect for Hyman."

"Why, I've hardly ever said two words to the man. I've just handled whatever he asked me to." Hyman looked amazed. "I've done as much for all our clients."

"That's what he said. You always did just as he asked, with honor and honesty." Simon's eyes were full of tears.

"Well, God bless Mr. Elkin," said Rebecca. "See, Hyman, I told you I had faith in my brothers' reputations."

"This certainly will help," said Hyman, "but we'll still have to sell the house. It will be a long time before the Gratz brothers will be back where they were."

"So we'll sell," said Rebecca. "We were getting root-bound, anyway." She smiled happily at her brothers. "It's only money; it could be something more important."

And the four weary men couldn't help but smile back at her.

CHAPTER EIGHTEEN

Home and Family

NEVER IN HER LIFE HAD REBECCA BEEN SO BUSY. THEIR NEW home at Number 2 Boston Row was not as spacious as the old one, and just getting settled was a major task.

"A parlour we don't need," she said, inspecting the place, "but a library we must have. This parlour will be our library. How does that sound, Miriam?"

"Just fine, Aunt Becky, we never used the parlour, anyway."

"I think that front hall bedroom will do for Uncle Hyman and Uncle Jo. Uncle Jac can take the one off the kitchen."

"Where will we sleep, Aunt Becky?" Little Horace tugged at her skirt.

"Well, there are three large bedrooms upstairs. The girls can have one, the boys another, and I'll take the third."

"Aunt Becky, we'll be awfully crowded," said nephew Simon.

"Well, I'll take Horace in with me. He won't mind. I'll get him a trundle bed."

"What's a trundle bed?"

"It's a little bed you can slide under Aunt Becky's big one. You'll love it, Horace." Miriam leaned down to reassure him.

"I'll like it as long as nobody forgets and pushes me under the bed," said Horace.

"Who could forget you?" laughed Rebecca. "You wouldn't let us."

That Friday night when they all sat down in the tiny dining room, Hyman looked troubled.

"What is the matter, Brother?" said Rebecca.

"Nothing, it's too crowded, isn't it?"

"Not crowded, just cozy," Rebecca said with a reassuring smile. She handed Hyman a huge platter of *Chalah*. He took one of the large slices of the bread and broke it into pieces, passing one to each child.

Each one held the piece of bread and watched Hyman. He looked down. The silver wine cup stood in its accustomed place by his plate, the same silver wine cup Michael Gratz had always used, filled to the brim with rich purple wine. Everything was the same, he thought, as he looked at Rebecca. This is the same Friday night meal Mama always made, laid on the white cloth Mama always used. Inwardly he thanked Rebecca. He raised the cup to recite the words of the *kiddush*. "Blessed art thou, O Lord our God, Ruler of the Universe, who created the fruit of the vine."

The children chorused after him, sipping from their small glasses of grape juice as Hyman drank the wine. Then he picked up the piece of *Chalah:*

"Blessed art Thou, O Lord our God, Ruler of the Universe, for bringing forth food upon this earth."

The children chanted this also, and as he bit into the bread, they did.

Rebecca's eyes shone in the candlelight.

101

"Hyman, we are lucky," she said.

"You're right, Sister," he said, "you're right!"

On Saturday morning they walked together to temple. People smiled, watching brother and sister walk along with the brood of children. Everyone knew them and marveled at the handsome group.

Rebecca led the girls to the gallery, and Hyman took the boys with him. He sat them all in front of the pulpit so that he could watch them while he read from the Torah.

"Uncle Hyman knows so much," whispered Miriam.

"Indeed he does," said Rebecca.

"I'd like to marry a man like him," said Sara.

"So should I," said Miriam.

"Ssh, girls," said Rebecca, pleased at the way in which the nieces loved their uncle.

"You must be very proud of such fine children," commented one of the older women to Rebecca.

"Oh, indeed I am," she replied.

"It is so wonderful the way an aunt will sacrifice her life for her nieces and nephews."

"I am giving up nothing," responded Rebecca. "These children are my life."

"Yes, that's what I always say." The women moved away, still chattering absent-mindedly.

"What does she mean, Aunt Becky?" asked Horace, tugging at his aunt's wide skirts.

"Nothing, my dear. She is only a foolish woman with a wagging tongue."

"She means, silly, that Aunt Becky can't get married on account of us," interposed Miriam.

"Why not?"

"Who'd want all of us?"

"Are we so bad?" Tears began to gather in Horace's eyes.

"Of course, you're not, my sweet," interrupted Rebecca, trying to put an end to the conversation.

"It is true, Aunt Becky, no man would ask to marry you with us around."

"What is the matter with us?" asked Horace in his small quavering voice.

"Nothing, silly," answered Miriam. "It's just that we are children, and lots of people, particularly unmarried gentlemen, think that children are a nuisance. We eat a lot and we're noisy and we ask silly questions and we always have things like measles and mumps and. . . ." Miriam's voice broke with her tears.

"We can't help it!" Horace and the others chorused with wails.

"Of course, you can't, my darlings, and no one wants you to be any different. Tell me, now, what's a few measles and mumps between friends?" Rebecca leaned down and kissed Horace on his small button nose.

"Aunt Becky, you must be serious and face facts," protested Miriam.

"Must I face them right here in the street?"

"Auntie, you're not serious. We're standing in the way of your living your own life."

"Miriam, I want you to stop this nonsense, and I never want to hear another word about this again. Do you all hear?" The small heads all bobbed affirmatively. The very seriousness of their faces made her smile, and they all smiled in return. "You listen to me. You all are mine. God gave you to me and when He did that He gave me all the joys and blessings any woman could want. This is the life I want to live, the life I love, and I don't want to hear you or anyone else making other plans for me. Understood?"

Again the heads nodded and the smiles shone like so many bright rainbows after warm spring showers.

"Come, let's go home," and with that Rebecca took Horace by the hand and led her family back home.

103

CHAPTER NINETEEN

Sunday School

HOME WAS STILL HOME IN SPITE OF EVERYTHING—A WARM, wonderful place that followed the pattern set by Rebecca's father and mother.

What wonderful training they had all been given, she thought! What a shame that all children couldn't have the privilege of living close to the teachings of God. This thought repeated itself over and over in her mind, especially on Saturday morning when she watched Hyman call their boys up to the Torah. The girls, too, could participate in the service beautifully, and they chanted with the voices of angels. Even little Horace chimed in with the *Shema,* which he had learned from his brothers.

"All children should have this kind of training," said Rebecca as she and Hyman walked home with the children after Sabbath services.

"You're right," said Hyman, absent-mindedly, concentrating more on enjoying the warm spring day.

"We should do something."

"Now, Becky?"

"Well, we should."

"Why we?"

"Because we are the ones who think it's important. I could start a little school right in our library. . . ." Rebecca's mind already raced ahead with plans.

"Becky, you tried once before, and it didn't work."

That was true. Years before Rebecca had tried to organize a small Hebrew class for children, but it met with no success.

"It's different now, Hyman. I'm older and I've had much more experience with children."

"You certainly have," Hyman agreed.

"And I've been watching Reverend Brown's experiment at his church."

"Church?"

"Yes, he has a Sunday school for children."

"You couldn't run a school on Shabbat."

"I know that, Hyman. I want to run a Sunday school, instead."

Hyman looked at his sister. Her dark eyes were sparkling; he knew that there would be no stopping her. He sighed.

"What do you want me to do, Sister?" he said without too much enthusiasm.

"Now, Hyman. You know you're just as concerned as I am."

"I am?"

"Well, hear me out." Rebecca proceeded to tell him about Reverend Brown's experiment. Since most children were only free on Sunday, he had decided that that was the best day. Even the apprentices had to have Sunday off; it was the law.

"It sounds good, Rebecca."

"Of course, and a Sunday school would be a way of start-ing. . . ."

"Starting?" Hyman looked at her in amazement.

"You know they can't learn all they should in an hour a week, but someday perhaps there will be an every day school or a special academy. . . ." She went on unrolling the spindle of her dreams.

"Becky, let's only try for what we can accomplish. I assume that you know there will be expenses."

"Some of the children will be able to pay." Rebecca was thoughtful.

Hyman smiled. "But you are planning on taking care of those who can't, aren't you?"

Rebecca nodded. The Jewish children of Philadelphia had always been her concern. She felt that they were sadly neglected. True, the boys of wealthier families went to *cheder,* but the poorer ones had to work as apprentices. The girls learned only what their well-meaning and untrained mothers could give them— much of ritual but little of meaning or philosophy or interpretation.

Something had to be done. Didn't the Talmud say that the children were the builders of the future? They could be neglected no longer. She knew several of the ladies of the congregation who would help.

"I may not be successful, but I must try," Rebecca told herself.

Rebecca took her plans to Rabbi Isaac Leeser at the Mikveh Israel Synagogue. He sat at his desk, a dwarfed little man with hands so small they looked like a child's. In proportion, his head looked heavy and large.

He must have had the pox, thought Rebecca, looking at his heavy, coarsely pitted skin; he is a most unattractive man. Hurriedly, she began to speak, afraid that he might notice her careful scrutiny and read her thoughts. She had no desire to hurt this young man.

"Rabbi Leeser, I come to you because you are renowned as a

106

. . . the children were the builders of the future? . . .

biblical scholar," Rebecca said, sitting primly erect in a chair before his desk.

"I am honored, Miss Gratz." He looked at her keenly through his heavy octagonal spectacles.

"You know who I am?" Rebecca was surprised since she had never before spoken to the young man.

"Of course. I have seen you in the gallery every Saturday morning with your pretty nieces. And I know both your brothers well." His voice was so pleasant that Rebecca began to forget his small stature and his general unattractiveness.

"Rabbi Leeser, I have gone to all of the ladies I know. There are several of us who are engaged in charitable work. We call ourselves the Female Hebrew Benevolent Society," she paused for breath.

"I know the group," he answered with a smile. "Wonderful, dedicated ladies."

"Well," Rebecca proceeded, "they have agreed to help, to donate their time as instructors. But they need help to plan efficient courses of instruction. I am sure you can understand that."

"Of course." He sounded doubtful.

"We planned to meet with the groups of children only on Sunday, and with only one day a week we must make the most of our time."

"Miss Gratz, are you proposing a Sunday school for the Congregation Mikveh Israel?" He stood up, looking so much like a little gnome that he seemed absurd.

"No, not just for our children; for all the children of Philadelphia." She was determined to tell him everything.

He slammed his little fist on the desk. "Miss Gratz, I cannot help you. If I aid you in getting a Sunday school at this synagogue, I will never get a day school. Parents will feel that if their children can be taught in one day, they do not need more."

Rebecca's face reddened with anger but she answered in a low tone, "And so, because this idea interferes with your plans, you are willing to let the children have nothing. I do not want to hinder your plans. All I want is to help the Jewish children of Philadelphia. We will have our own quarters and our own funds. All I asked of you was your help. While you work and plan and dream of your grand school, there are Jewish children all over Philadelphia who are learning nothing."

"The children of *this* synagogue are my responsibility," Rabbi Leeser argued.

Standing there, even angry, Rabbi Leeser did not lose the look of some small gargoyle, and Rebecca felt her heart fill with pity. She had heard the ladies of the congregation comment on his appearance; some even laughing at his rather pathetic ugliness; and as much as they might respect his scholarship, they avoided his company. For the most part, he devoted himself to his books and his work in the snyagogue, but Rebecca imagined that he must be very lonely. Hyman and Jo and Jac had remained bachelors from preference, never lacking for female admiration and attention, but this man was different.

He must be much younger than I, thought Rebecca, and yet he looks so old and withered. She dropped her voice to a gentler level.

"You are too good a Jew to say that, Rabbi Leeser. *All* the children of Philadelphia are our responsibility, especially all of the Jewish children. There is a need here which neither you nor I can deny." Rebecca sat quietly in her chair with her hands folded and waited.

He avoided her intent gaze. Weakly, he added another protest, "There will be objections, you know."

"Of course, but they are of little consequence. As I said, I have volunteer workers; I have been promised finances. All that is needed is the skill of a learned teacher who can help us to plan a program that will be worthwhile."

It may have been Rebecca's logic or her persistence; it may have been her manner, so respectful yet so determined; it may have been her charm. But whatever it was, Isaac Leeser suddenly made his decision.

"I will help you," he said, a new note of determination in his voice.

"Oh, I do thank you." Rebecca seized his hands in hers. "You are a good man and I am so grateful."

"Now," he said, as he sat down, "let me see how I can help you."

He began to pull out the drawers and to pile the desk high with papers and notebooks and pamphlets.

"Now, all of these will be useful," he said. "Your ladies can go through them carefully to familiarize themselves with content. Then I will meet with you all one day so that we can discuss procedure."

Rebecca nodded. Now Rabbi Leeser was speaking with assurance, all the proficiency that was his pouring out in a multitude of suggestions.

"We will, of course, need to compile a sort of catechism, a series of questions and answers that all the children can use. These young scholars will be at all levels of knowledge you know, and it will be up to us to establish a common denominator and proceed from there."

"I see," said Rebecca, aware that in his interest he had almost forgotten that she was there.

"We shall have to establish certain basics in each study group. When a child has achieved these, he may pass to a more advanced group. That will be the most efficient way to proceed."

It was an hour later before Rebecca left his office, her arms piled high with books and her head whirling with ideas. She knew that the enthusiasm she felt would make all the work of the Sunday school easy. The fact that the school could offer well-planned and authoritative material made the whole project so much more worthwhile. She had the feeling, too, that today's help was not the last that Rabbi Leeser would give.

110

The little man reminded her of an anecdote her father used to tell about a beautiful lady who had remarked to an ancient wise man that it was indeed a freak of nature to place so much wisdom in ugliness.

"And what does your father keep his wine in?" demanded the wrinkled old man.

"An earthen jug," she answered.

"Why?" the wise man persisted.

The lady shrugged. She did not know.

"I'll tell you. It's because wine kept in precious metal turns sour. So it is that wisdom is only safe in ugliness; for in ugliness there is no vanity, which is wisdom's great enemy."

★　★　★　★

March 4, 1838, was Rebecca's fifty-seventh birthday and it marked the official opening of the Hebrew Sunday school, the first of its kind in the United States. Rebecca, herself, was superintendent, assisted by a staff of six volunteer teachers. For the first time, also, the doors of a Hebrew school were opened to girls as well as to boys. Many comments were passed, and many shook their heads at such an innovation.

Rabbi Leeser arrived at Rebecca's office shortly before nine that first morning, eager to be of help.

"Does everything go well, Miss Gratz?"

"Very well, Rabbi Leeser."

"How many students have you enrolled?"

"Over fifty have expressed a desire to join our group." Rebecca's dark eyes gleamed with excitement.

"That is most encouraging. I only pray that I will live to see the day when my school opens its doors to that many students." Rebecca knew that her friend was downcast because as yet his plans for an all-day school had come to nothing.

"Rabbi Leeser, you will have your school. In the meantime,

these children will get the benefit of your vast store of knowledge. As my father often said, 'Half a loaf is better than none.' "

Rabbi Leeser laughed, "I would like to have known your father. He seems to have been quite a talmudic scholar. How much wisdom and philosophy he left with you!"

"Ah, he did. He had wisdom and strength and love and he was always there to help us. In fact, he himself often said that a man could only develop a philosophy when he learned to make the best of a situation he could do nothing about." Rebecca smiled as she remembered Michael Gratz's gentle reasoning.

"You will not mind if I keep working for *my* school?" Rabbi Leeser searched Rebecca's face closely.

"Mind? Rabbi Leeser, my friend, Isaac, how could I mind? Has anyone a monopoly on learning? I would be happy to be the first to help you as you have helped me. The best we can offer here is a make-shift, a beginning. I will rejoice when the day comes when you will be able to use your skills to the fullest."

CHAPTER TWENTY

"As Miss Gratz Had Done"

REBECCA'S LITTLE SUNDAY SCHOOL FLOURISHED. IT WAS LOCATED on Zone Street over the Phoenix Hose Company, and many of the children would dawdle on their way to class to look at the fire apparatus, to run their hands over the shiny metal of the wagons, to ring the big gong, to pet the huge spotted dog who was the mascot for the friendly men who loved to indulge the youngsters and answer their questions.

But suddenly, there would be a familiar step and a familiar voice and the children would scamper up the stairs.

"Time for class," was all Miss Gratz had to say. The years had been kind to Rebecca. Her hair was still dark and her figure still slim. She held herself erect and walked with sureness and dignity.

Her black bengaline dresses were more severe than stylish,

touched only with a frill of lace at the throat. She wore a small white lace cap on her hair.

"Children," she would say, "let us begin," and the children would file in and slide along the long yellow benches and sit at attention.

On Rebecca's desk were a Bible and Watt's *Hymn Book* as well as a handbell and a penny box to hold contributions for the poor. As the children quieted, Rebecca would begin:

"Come, ye children, hearken unto me, and I will teach you love of the Lord."

The children would lower their heads in prayer, and then they would hearken as Miss Gratz read a chapter from the Scriptures in her clear voice. Together they would go to lands far from Philadelphia, to the green valleys near Galilee, to the home of Abraham, Isaac, and Jacob. Too soon the hour would be over, a Hebrew hymn would be sung, and the lesson finished for another week.

Long after the children had gone, Rebecca would sit at her desk preparing new lessons for the coming weeks. Little Sara Jane, Richea's daughter, would sit on one of the benches pasting strips of paper over passages Rebecca had marked in the Scripture lessons published by the Christian Sunday School Union.

"Aunt Becky, why am I covering these questions and answers?" Sara Jane would say.

"That is a Christian catechism," Rebecca would answer. "And that material is not what I want to teach." Sara Jane would go back to her pasting, not quite satisfied.

"Too bad we don't have Jewish books," the little girl would mutter.

"We will, we will. Everything in due time," was Aunt Rebecca's answer.

It was Rabbi Leeser who filled this great need for works designed specifically for Jewish children. His *Catechism for Younger Children* designed as a familiar exposition of the Jewish religion was finished in 1839, and dedicated to his friend, "Miss Rebecca Gratz, Superintendent of the Sunday School for Israelites in Philadelphia."

Her friendship had come to mean a great deal to him, and her willingness to help others had been an inspiration to him. And so, with the catechism went a small note:

> *Esteemed friend,*
> I have long wished for an opportunity to acknowledge my indebtedness for the approval you kindly bestowed upon my youthful labors, and the frequent marks of friendship I received from you since my lot has been cast in this place. As this little has been undertaken to assist your efforts which so far have been crowned with single success to form an institution whence the waters of life flow alike into the rich and the poor. . . .

Rabbi Leeser's catechism was followed by a reader, the first work of its kind, meant especially for Hebrew Sunday schools. This was followed by other teaching aids. Rebecca, too, was keeping notebooks of her school's operation. As more schools were set up in Philadelphia and in other cities in other parts of the country, they were able to use the pattern established by Rebecca Gratz and Isaac Leeser. In Charleston, South Carolina, in Richmond, Virginia, and in New York City, other Hebrew Sunday schools were established by other women, inspired by the example set by Rebecca.

Rebecca minimized her efforts humbly even though she professed to be most gratified at the evident improvement of a large class of children in religious knowledge. She found it influenced their conduct and manners and was becoming important in the minds of their parents.

By 1854—years after it was first opened—the Sunday school had moved to free rooms donated by the Hebrew Education Society.

The rooms were not as suitable as their first quarters but the saving on rent allowed for other growing expenditures.

Sara Jane was no longer a small girl dedicated to menial tasks; she was now a teacher herself. There were many more children and on Sara Jane's desk was Rabbi Leeser's catechism and his new edition of the Holy Scriptures which replaced the old King James Bible.

Miss Sim'ha Pixotto, one of the teachers, had also written a set of scriptural questions that were in use.

On the walls were new maps of Jerusalem and scrolls showing the Ten Commandments. Rabbi Leeser was a constant visitor bringing with him a young friend, a Mister Morais. Both were always ready to lead a hymn or substitute for an absent teacher.

The coming of Purim marked the time for the annual examination. It was a kind of anniversary, too, for it marked the date of the school's opening. Each child was called up to Miss Gratz's desk to recite. One teacher stood in the center of the room, asking questions. The first prizes were Bibles, and two were given to each class.

Miss Gratz would hand the books to the children with a gracious smile. She had donated them herself and lovingly inscribed each for its owner. As the proceedings ended, each child would file out happily, each having been given an orange or a pretzel.

By 1858, Rebecca, after twenty years of untiring devotion to the school, took the advice offered her and had officers assist her in her work. She was seventy-seven years old, but her sight and memory were still keen. She was to be in weekly attendance several years longer until she resigned the presidency to her devoted friend, Miss Louisa Hart, who continued to do everything "as Miss Gratz would have done."

CHAPTER TWENTY-ONE

Hear, O Israel

REBECCA NEVER LOST INTEREST IN THOSE IN NEED. WHEREVER she could help, she was the first to volunteer her services. She worked for the Hebrew Sewing Society, the Fuel Society, and for the various groups being set up to aid the growing population of Jewish immigrants in Philadelphia. At seventy-four she helped to establish a Jewish foster home and an orphan asylum and became its first president. Her own children, her beloved nieces and nephews, were grown and married. She wrote them all constantly, advising and consoling them, exulting in their triumphs, but never burdening them with her problems or the thoughts of her advancing years. They were a family to be proud of, everyone a product of the fine traditions of the Gratz family and of America.

Frances's son, Henry Etting, was a commodore in the United States Navy. The Etting grandsons had distinguished themselves also as naval officers. Richea's son, Isaac Hays, had become one of the country's great oculists and his son was an eminent physician.

Rebecca's children, as she always called them, had done her proud, and how pleased Rachel would have been with all of them! Simon was one of the foremost physicians in the country, a professor of Obstetrics in the Missouri Medical College. Sara and Miriam and Becky had married well. Horace, her favorite, had served his country in the war with Mexico and returned to become a prominent member of the community. Edmund, the daring one, had gone West with the forty-niners.

Rebecca's heart followed them all, but she did not cling to their paths of adventure. Instead she kept to her own chosen way, leaving them free for their own endeavors.

Horace still remained close to Aunt Becky, coming to visit as often as he could, but just as often finding her not at home. It worried him that she might be doing too much.

"Where have you been?" he demanded on one such occasion after he had sat for what seemed hours in the drawing room waiting for her return.

"Horace, I've been out on business!" Her eyes were snapping with anger, and her tone was sharp.

"Some man came to me several days ago with a little boy, a baby, just five years old. He had promised the child's dying mother to care for him, but he had tired of the responsibility. I told him I would make the necessary arrangements but he never returned. Only today I learned that he had left the little fellow in a house of refuge to save any fee we might ask."

"And where were you, Aunt Becky?" asked Horace.

"I went to get that child. Imagine leaving him among convicts to save a few paltry dollars!"

"And you paid the few dollars and deposited him in your precious orphans' home, I gather." Horace shook his head in bemused admiration.

"I did. That child wasn't to stay in that awful place for another

118

hour, for another moment." Her voice trembled as she sat down. "I'm an old woman, Horace," she said, "I can't do as much as I used to."

"I'll bet you're one old woman that little chap was glad to see. I can remember how much my Aunt Becky meant to another motherless little boy." Horace leaned down to kiss her white curls, not saying one word of caution about her not giving so much of herself. He knew this was the way she had to be.

And so she continued doing as much as she could for the Hebrew Orphans of Philadelphia. Her half-century of experience with the Foster Home had given her a wealth of practical knowledge that she gladly gave to the Jewish community. Cities all over the United States sent Jewish orphans to this new home that reflected in its by-laws and its operation a sincere desire to raise children to be devout Jews. Rebecca lived to serve—performing endless tasks, doing administrative work, looking for contributions, and aiding in getting volunteers who would also give their time.

Now her hair was white and her lovely skin showed the marks of age, but her eyes still glowed with passionate dedication and with the sparks of interest that kindled whenever she heard a pathetic story. Many times, she heard her mother's voice saying, "In doing good works, there is happiness." Yes, in good deeds, there was indeed happiness.

She thought of her family, of Hyman and Jo and Jac; she had been their housekeeper. People had often felt sorry for her, the lonely sister, but she had never been lonely. Her brothers had given her a reason for doing all the things a woman loves to do that are part of the task of keeping a home. And the children, Rachel's children, every one of them had been a joy. She remembered the parties she had planned for them and how the house would fill with laughter. How empty it would have been without them!

In her mind, she could see Horace as a baby with his rocking

119

horse, head thrown back, eyes aglow with childish excitement. And Isaac, curly-haired Isaac with his head bent over his books, watching her out of the corner of his eye to see whether she was watching him. Those wonderful children had filled her years.

Her mind flooded with the memories of other children, too—the children in the Foster Home, the ones whose small charred bodies she had seen carried from the orphanage, the ones in her Sunday school who had become educators in the Jewish community. She remembered how often her heart had swelled in pride as they answered questions of faith in unison. "What formed you child and what made you live?"

"God did my life and spirit give."

★   ★   ★   ★

In 1861, the children—the nieces and nephews, the grandnieces and grandnephews—were scattered in all parts of the country taking their part in the Great War between the States. Some aided the Union, some the Confederacy; things would never be the same. The news of secession shocked Rebecca, and she prayed that Kentucky, the home of her brother Ben and his family, would remain in the Union.

"The seceders will bring ruin on us all," she would say. "They will tear our country in two. The leaders in South Carolina are evil."

Rebecca sympathized with the slaves, and with her rare insight saw more in the situation than most people. "The master," she wrote, "is as enslaved as the slave; he is so dependent that he is no more free than his chattel."

But her greatest fear was for those near and dear to her, divided now by this horrible struggle. She could feel no elation at victories, victories steeped in tragedy for so many.

But there was no turning back. In August of 1861, Rebecca received word that Ben's youngest son, Gary, was killed at the

Battle of Wilson Creek, Missouri. She hardly believed it possible as she wrote words of consolation to her brother.

> May God help you in your time of adversity. There is so little I can say that will help at such a moment. When such a young life is trampled, we who are left feel only the emptiness and the pain. . . .

★ ★ ★ ★

Rebecca lived to see the war end and a kind of peace restored. Age was beginning to triumph over her hardy spirit, and she spent more and more of her time in remembrance. Her life had been good and rich and satisfying; she was content with the lot God had seen fit to give her.

At the age of eighty-eight, Rebecca passed into the hands of her Maker, and her last words were an echo of the feeling that had always been in her heart.

> I, Rebecca Gratz, of the City of Philadelphia, being of sound health of body and mind, advanced in the vale of years, declare this to be my last will and testament. I commit my spirit to God who gave it, relying on His mercy and redeeming love, and believing with a firm and perfect faith in the religion of my fathers. . . .

> Hear, O Israel, the Lord, our God, the Lord is one.